OVER THE HILLS

OF

MY BOOK HOUSE

EDITED BY

OLIVE BEAUPRÉ MILLER

PUBLISHERS

THE BOOK HOUSE for CHILDREN

CHICAGO

CONTENTS

PAGE

ABRAHAM LINCOLN . . . . Rosemary and Stephen Vincent Benét 128

ALL ABOUT COLUMBUS 112

BABE OF BETHLEHEM, THE . . . . . From The Bible 222

BOOTS AND HIS BROTHERS . . . . Sir George Webb Dasent 156

BOYHOOD OF ROBERT FULTON, THE 48

CASEY JONES . . . . . A Song of the Railroad Men 64

DICK WHITTINGTON AND HIS CAT . . . An English Legend 33

DIVERTING HISTORY OF JOHN GILPIN, THE . . William Cowper 76

FIRST THANKSGIVING DAY, THE . . Alice Williams Brotherton 113

FOURTH OF JULY, THE . . . . Olive Beaupré Miller 127

GEORGE WASHINGTON AND THE FIRST AMERICAN FLAG . . . 116

GETTYSBURG ADDRESS . . . . . Abraham Lincoln 137

HEIDI IN THE ALPINE PASTURE . . . . Johanna Spyri 147

HIAWATHA'S CHILDHOOD . . . . Henry Wadsworth Longfellow 182

IN COLUMBUS' TIME . . . . . Annette Wynne 112

JACK AND THE BEANSTALK . . . . An English Folk Tale 20

JAMIE WATT AND THE TEA KETTLE 45

LITTLE BOY IN PARIS, A 68

LITTLE DIAMOND AND THE NORTH WIND . . George MacDonald 186

LITTLE GULLIVER . . . . . Louisa M. Alcott 103

LITTLE SHEPHERD'S SONG . . . William Alexander Percy 139

NUREMBERG STOVE, THE . . . . . Louise de la Ramée 162

PONY ENGINE AND THE PACIFIC EXPRESS, THE . William Dean Howells 54

		PAGE
SEA GULL, THE	Mary Howitt	111
STEAMBOAT AND THE LOCOMOTIVE, THE . . .	Gelett Burgess	96
STORY ABOUT ABE LINCOLN, A		129
STORY OF TOM THUMB, THE	An English Folk Tale	11
SWITCH YARD, THE	John Curtis Underwood	53
THUMBELISA	Hans Christian Andersen	206
WE THANK THEE	Ralph Waldo Emerson	115
WHERE GO THE BOATS?	Robert Louis Stevenson	138
WHY THE SEA IS SALT	Gudrun Thorne-Thomsen	140
A Norse Folk Tale		
WILBUR WRIGHT AND ORVILLE WRIGHT	Rosemary and Stephen Vincent Benét	66

The Story of Tom Thumb
AN ENGLISH FOLK TALE

LONG ago in the days of the great King Arthur, an honest ploughman lived with his wife in a neat, cozy, little cottage. They would have been very happy except that they had no children.

"I should be the happiest woman in the world," said the wife one day, "if only I had a son. Even if he were no bigger than my husband's thumb, I would be satisfied."

Sometime after this, the good woman's wish was fulfilled. She did indeed have a son; and, strange to say, he was not one bit bigger than his father's thumb. The Queen of the Fairies, wishing to see the child, flew in at the window when he was but a few days old, and found his mother feeding him out of the cup of an acorn.

As soon as the Queen saw the little fellow, she kissed him and gave him the name of Tom Thumb. Then she sent for some of her fairies to come and dress him according to her orders. They made him a little hat of an oak leaf, his shirt was of spider's web, his jacket of thistledown, and his trousers of tiny feathers. His stockings were made of apple rind and his shoes of a mouse's skin.

Tom never grew any bigger than his father's thumb; but he was a brave, merry little fellow, so his parents loved him dearly. One day his mother was making a batter pudding and she put him in an empty eggshell to keep him out of mischief. But Tom, being anxious to see how she stirred up the batter, climbed out of the shell and up the slippery side of the bowl. The next thing he knew, he lost his footing and plunged head over heels into the batter.

His mother never noticed him, but stirred him right into the pudding. Then she dumped him into the pudding bag and put him in the kettle to boil. The batter filled Tom's mouth and prevented him from crying out, but he kicked and struggled with all his might to

get himself free. His
mother, seeing her
pudding dance madly
around in the pot as
if it were alive, seized
it in alarm and threw
it out the window.
Just then a tinker
passed by; and, as he saw a nice-
looking pudding coming his way,
he picked it up and started to eat
it. But Tom, having by that time
freed his mouth of the batter,
began to cry aloud: "Let me go!
Let me go, Tom the Tinker!"

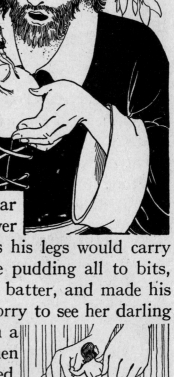

The Tinker was so startled to hear
the pudding talk, that he flung it over
the hedge and ran away as fast as his legs would carry
him. But the fall had broken the pudding all to bits,
so Tom crept out, all covered with batter, and made his
way home. His mother was very sorry to see her darling
in such a state, but she put him in a
teacup and washed him off clean; then
she kissed him and put him to bed.

Soon after this, Tom's mother went
one day to milk her cow in the pasture
and she took Tom along with her. It
was a very windy day; and, in order to

make sure that Tom should not blow away, she tied him to a thistle with a strand of fine thread. The cow was peacefully eating; but she soon spied Tom's oak-leaf hat and, thinking it a choice morsel, she took up the little fellow and the thistle at a mouthful. When the cow began to chew, Tom had great difficulty to keep out of the way of her teeth and her tongue, but he called out boldly, "Mother! Mother!"

"My dear little Tommy, where are you?" cried his mother. "I'm here in the red cow's mouth!" Tom answered. At that, the cow, surprised at the odd tickling as of something moving in her throat, opened her mouth. Down her tongue slid Tom as on a toboggan slide. His mother caught him in her apron and ran off home at once.

OVER THE HILLS

Often Tom went to the fields with his father; and, as he was anxious to be of use, he one day begged to be allowed to take home the horse and cart.

"You! Why you couldn't even reach up to the top of the horse's hoofs!" laughed the father. "How do you think you are ever going to hold the reins?"

"Oh," answered Tom quite confidently, "I don't need to hold the reins. I'll just sit in the horse's ear and call out which way he is to go!"

The father was amazed to find his son so bold and clever, so he put Tom in the horse's ear and off he went.

"Yeo-hup! Yeo-hup!" cried Tom and he guided the horse so well, that he reached home in no time at all. Tom's mother was greatly surprised when she saw the horse arrive at the cottage with no one in sight as a driver; but Tom called out, "Mother! Mother, take me down! I'm in the horse's ear!"

"Now just to think of a little man like you driving a great big beast like that!" cried the mother and she was so pleased with what Tom had done, that she lifted him carefully down and gave him a whole big red currant for his supper.

Seeing how helpful his son could be, the father now made him a little whip of a barley straw, so he could sometimes drive the cattle home. As he was in the field thus at work one day, a raven spied him and picked him up—soaring high in the air and carrying him away. He dropped him, at last, from his talons into the top of a tree near a giant's castle. Pretty soon, out came the giant for a walk on the terrace. Mistaking Tom for the fruit of the tree, he plucked him off the branch and opened his mouth to swallow him. But just then along through the air came the Queen of the Fairies, in a chariot drawn by flying mice. Snatching Tom from the giant's hand, she placed him beside her and drove off to Fairyland.

In that lovely country Tom spent many happy days, being well-entertained by the fairies; but, after a time, the Queen dressed him in a new little suit of bright green, and sent him floating on a lively breeze straight to King Arthur's palace. As Tom was flying over the palace yard, the king's cook passed along below with a great bowl of the king's favorite dish, frumenty. At that moment the breeze dropped Tom and he fell plumb into the middle of the bowl, making the cook drop it with a smash and spill all the king's dainty frumenty.

"Help! Help! Thieves!" cried the cook who was a red-faced, coarse-grained fellow.

Swearing that Tom had meant to play this trick on him, the cook put Tom in a mousetrap, intending to keep him there till he could make complaint of him before the king.

But the cat, seeing something moving in the cage, thought Tom was a mouse; so she rolled the cage about between her paws till she broke it and set Tom loose. Then Tom ran off and hid in an empty snail's shell. There he stayed until he grew hungry. Peeping out in search of some means to get food, he saw a butterfly alight on a nearby flower; so he sprang at once astride the butterfly's back and the little creature flew with him up in the air, flitting from flower to flower. At last, attracted by a light in the king's dining-room, the butterfly flew in the window. King, queen, and nobles saw him and tried to catch him, but they could not. Nevertheless, with the butterfly's darting to keep out of reach, Tom—having neither saddle nor bridle—lost his seat on the butterfly's back and fell sprawling on the table.

King, queen, and nobles all spied the little man at once, and everyone was delighted with him. Far from punishing him for spoiling his frumenty, the king gave him half a blackberry for his supper, and he soon became a great favorite. His tricks and gambols and lively words amused the whole court; and, when the king rode out, he often took Tom along, he thought so much of his company. If it happened to rain, Tom would creep in the king's pocket and sleep there quite cozily till the rain was over.

At length King Arthur ordered a little chair to be made, so that Tom might sit before him on the table. And he also caused to be built for Tom a palace of gold, with a door just an inch in width, and he gave him a little golden coach with six white mice to draw it.

But Tom still thought of his mother and father; and, one day, he asked the king to let him pay them a visit. King Arthur not only consented, but, when he heard that Tom's parents were poor, he led him to the treasury where he kept all his gold and told him he might take home as much money as he could carry. With difficulty Tom dragged out a three-penny piece, and loaded it on his back. Then he toiled along the road for two days beneath his burden before he reached his father's cottage.

Tom's mother met him at the door and she could not thank him enough for having taken so much trouble as to drag home a three-penny piece, all for love of his father and mother. She placed him in a cozy walnut shell beside the fire; and she feasted him for three days, until he had consumed the whole of a hazelnut. When he had thoroughly rested, his duty told him the time had come for him to return to court. So he said good-bye to his mother and father and set off on his way.

As soon as he reached the castle, King Arthur made him a knight. Sir Thomas Thumb he was now called, and the king gave him a needle for a sword and a mouse for a horse. Thus armed and thus mounted, Tom rode with the king and his knights, and all enjoyed a hearty laugh at sight of Sir Thomas and his prancing steed. One day as they passed a farmhouse, a big black cat jumped out and rushed on Tom and his mouse. But Tom drew his needle at once and so boldly defended himself that he kept the cat at needle's length till one of the king's knights came and carried him safely home.

Thus Sir Thomas Thumb held his own in the world very bravely and was withal so merry, that he won the affection of all. In later years he often sang:

"My name is Tom Thumb;
From the fairies I've come;
When King Arthur shone,
His court was my home.
In me he delighted,
By him I was knighted.
Did you never once hear
Of Sir Thomas Thumb?"

Jack and the Beanstalk

AN ENGLISH FOLK TALE

ONCE a poor woman lived in a cottage with her only son, Jack, a good enough fellow at heart, but heedless and unthinking. The boy worked when he chose and followed his own pleasure when he chose; so, as his mother was poor, she had to support them both by selling everything she had. At last nothing remained but one cow. "Oh, you heedless boy," the mother cried one day, "while you were amusing yourself in the village, we have eaten up everything we had. There's not even a crumb of bread left. Nothing remains but my cow."

Jack was ashamed for a moment, but, as he grew hungrier and hungrier, he began to tease his mother to let him sell the cow. Knowing nothing else to do, the mother sadly consented, bidding her son use good judgment and get a fair price for the cow. So Jack started out for market, driving bossy before him. Soon he fell in with a butcher, who asked why he was driving the cow away from home. Jack said he was going to sell her. Then the butcher took from a bag some wonderful, bright-colored beans, which caught Jack's fancy at once. Know-

ing the lad's easy temper, the butcher offered to give the beans in exchange for the cow. In an instant the foolish boy had forgotten their great need at home, he thought only how pleased he would be to have the bright-colored beans. So the bargain was struck in a moment, and the butcher went off with the cow. Rushing home in great excitement, Jack told his mother what he had done. "You foolish boy," cried the mother, bursting into tears. "We have nothing at all to eat, yet you have sold my good cow for a few paltry beans that tickled your fancy. Go play with your childish playthings, we shall have no supper tonight." And she tossed the beans out the back door, scattering them everywhere.

For the first time in his life, Jack was thoroughly sorry when he saw the hot tears his mother was weeping because of his folly. Those silly, useless beans! How foolish he had been! He had no further wish now to find amuse-

This old English folk tale has been charmingly re-written by John Erskine as a fairy opera, with music composed by Louis Gruenberg.

ment for himself, but went off to his room and started in to think. He remembered how good his mother had always been to him and how he had repaid her with idleness and folly! He sat a long time in sorrow and resolved the very next day to set himself to work.

Early the following morning, he started to get out of bed, when he saw, all at once, that in the night something strange and green had grown up past his window. Hurrying to the lattice, he opened it and looked out. There he saw a great vine shooting up and up and up! Up it grew to the sky. His beans had taken root! They had sprung up in this vine! And the stalks of enormous thickness had so entwined themselves that they seemed to form a ladder. Jack looked up as far as he could to see the top of the thing, but it seemed to be lost in the clouds. He tried it and found it firm. Then a great idea struck him. This ladder, grown from the beans which he had so thoughtlessly taken, must be meant for him to climb! He was sorry for what he had done. He wished to make up for his folly and he told himself that this ladder must have been given him as a wonderful chance to climb to some new task or adventure wherein he might attain something of real use to his mother.

Full of this idea, Jack hastened to tell his mother. She would gladly have held him back, but she saw that at last the time had come when she must let him go forth to make his way in the world. So the boy put his foot on the bottom of the ladder and started to climb at once.

He climbed and he climbed toward the sky.
He grew very weary, indeed; but, still, he persisted in climbing. At last he reached the top of
the vine and stepped off into a barren, rocky,
and lonely country where there was not a tree,
not a house, nor a living creature anywhere
to be seen. The boy sat down on a stone. He
was tired and very hungry, for he had had
nothing to eat since noon of the day before;
but, still, he thought chiefly now of his hope
that some worthy task was awaiting him in
this place. Then, lo, as he sat thinking, a very
queer, little, old lady appeared all at once before
him. She wore a pointed cap trimmed with
white ermine, her hair streamed loose on her
shoulders, and she carried a wand in her hand.

"I am a fairy, Jack," the little, old lady said.
"Your sorrow for your folly and idleness and
your wish, at last, to perform some really
worthy task made your worthless beans
sprout and form a ladder to bring you
to me. Had you done nothing more than
look at the giant beanstalk and stupidly
wonder about it, you would never have
found me. But you showed an inquir-
ing mind, great courage, and enterprise;
therefore, you deserve to rise. It is my
business to tell you what great things

you have to do here. The story I shall relate, your mother has never dared tell you; but, though you are only a lad, the chance lies before you now to do the deeds of a man."

Jack held his breath with astonishment.

"Your father was a rich man with a very generous nature," the little, old lady went on. "He was kind to everyone and helped, not only those who came and asked his aid, but all who needed anything. So good a man was he, that he aroused the anger of a giant who lived nearby. So wicked and cruel was this creature, that he could not bear to hear others talked of for their goodness. Hearing, one day, that your parents were about to visit a friend at some little distance from home, he waylaid them on the road, seized them, and bound them with ropes. Then he drove out your father's servants and took possession of his castle. At this time, you, my lad, were only six months old, and, with your mother and father, you were cast by the giant into the deepest dungeon of your father's castle. There you all three lay for months; but, at last, the giant offered to set your mother free and let her take you away on condition that she would swear never to tell a single soul the story of her wrongs.

"To put it out of her power to do him any harm, the giant placed her on shipboard and sent her, with you in

her arms, far off to a distant land. There she was left
with no money and nothing to sell but some jewels which she
had hidden in her dress. Now the giant lives in this
country; your father's castle is here and, in it, your father
is still held a prisoner by the giant. It is you, who must
free your father and restore him to his rights. All the giant
has is yours. Regain what you can of it. You will meet
with many dangers and many difficulties, but you must
have courage at all times and always stick to your task.
Moreover, do nothing rashly, but think before you act.
Right and Justice are with you; and, if you go fearlessly
forward always standing your ground, you will find yourself one of those who are able to conquer giants."

As soon as she had spoken, the
Fairy disappeared, leaving Jack greatly
stirred by all that she had told him.
He started at once to go forward. On
and on he walked, although he came to
no dwelling. At length, as night came
on, he laid himself down to sleep beneath
the shelter of a rock. In the morning,
to his great joy, he saw not far away
the castle for which he was looking.
Now, greatly in need of food, he went
to the door and knocked. A huge
woman opened the door and listened
in great astonishment while he
begged for a bit to eat.

"It's most uncommon," she said, "to see any stranger here! It's all too well-known in these parts that my husband is a cruel giant! If you know what is good for you, you'll run away at once!"

Jack trembled with fear for a moment: he wanted to run away; but, then, he remembered the Fairy had told him to stand his ground. So he boldly asked for food again, offering in return to do any kind of work. For a moment, the woman considered. She, hereslf, drudged and labored from morning until night and was greatly in need of help. So, at last, she was persuaded and let Jack in the house.

They passed through a number of rooms, all very grandly furnished, but lonely-looking and dreary. Then they came to a long, dark gallery with a grating of iron on one side; and, beyond that, a dismal dungeon whence Jack could hear doleful sighs and the awful clanking of chains. His heart beat fast at the thought that his father must be confined there, and he grew more determined than ever to stick bravely to his task until he set him free.

The woman took Jack to the kitchen where a huge fire burned. There she bade him sit down and placed food and drink before him. And now, after all, he saw that she was a kindly woman—only much overworked and worried by the bullying of the giant. When he had finished his meal, she set him to work at scrubbing. All day long he worked, harder and more steadily than he had ever done in all his life before. At length when evening came, a thunderous knocking was heard that made the whole house shake.

So, early one morning, the boy once more started out to climb the magic beanstalk. When he reached the giant's mansion, the woman answered his knock just as she had before. Jack begged her for a night's lodging; and, though she scolded him roundly for taking her husband's hen, Jack well knew by this time that she was a kindly woman and he had no need to fear her. At last, she admitted the lad and gave him something to eat. Jack repaid her by working hard till they heard the giant thundering as usual at the gate. This time the woman hid the boy in the lumber closet. The  giant blustered in and went sniff, sniff, about and roared as he had before:

Fee—Fi—Fo—Fum,
I smell the blood of an Englishman!

But his wife once more reminded him that he had an Englishman in the dungeon, so the giant quieted down and consented to eat his supper. Then he ordered his wife to bring his bags of gold and silver. Jack peeped from his hiding-place and watched him count the treasure, which he had stolen from the lad's father. But at last he fell asleep and started in to snore. Then Jack crept out from the closet and approached him very quietly. All at once, a little dog

29

under the giant's chair began to bark furiously. The giant opened one eye. Jack seized the bags and ran! Down the beanstalk he raced and was soon back home again.

If his mother had been glad to see him come home safe before, this time she was doubly glad. And now with all the money bags, they were very well-off indeed. Still, with all the comfort at home, Jack never wished to remain there idling at his ease, while his father was in a dungeon.

So he climbed the beanstalk a third time. This time the giantess met him with a rougher manner than before, for her husband had been very hard on her when he found the money bags gone. It took much talking on Jack's part to persuade her to admit him; but, at last, she let him go to work and eat his supper as usual. When the giant came home, Jack was hidden in the copper kettle.

At once the great bully roared:

Fee—Fi—Fo—Fum,
I smell the blood of an Englishman!

And in spite of all his wife could say, he banged around the room, searching every nook and corner. Jack held his breath in suspense. The giant came to the kettle and put his hand on the lid. Jack thought his last hour had come, but no, the search ended here and the bully sat down by the fireside!

When he had eaten his supper, the giant ordered his wife to fetch him his magic harp. Jack peeped out from under the copper lid of the kettle and saw the woman bring the instrument. It was all carved of gold and, on the front, was the figure of a beautiful woman with wings. When the giant said, "Play!" the harp of its own accord played music so soft and melodious that Jack was filled with delight. But the giant soon tired of the music and, as usual, fell fast asleep. Climbing out of the kettle, Jack at once seized the harp. Then the harp began to cry loudly: "Master! Master! Master!" Jack thought it would waken the giant, and was almost ready to drop it, when he suddenly felt it turning as if alive in his arms. Directing itself by its wings, it pulled him right along with it. Not toward the outer gate, but back into the house— back toward the dungeons it went. "Master! Master!" it shouted, and soon it dragged Jack to the spot where he knew his father must be imprisoned. "Master! Master!" it twanged louder than before; and lo, a whitehaired old man appeared at the grating of one of the dungeons.

"My harp! Who bears you hither?" he cried.

Jack answered at once, "Thy son!"

"My son!" The man wept for joy.

"Harp! Harp! Play off my chains!" he commanded.

Such music as the harp played then! The chains fell with a crash from off the old man's feet.

"Harp! Harp! Play open my dungeon door!" The Harp played again, the door opened, Jack's father passed through in safety, and the two hurried down the gallery.

But by this time, great noise and commotion resounded from the kitchen. The giant was now wide awake, roaring

furiously for his harp. As Jack and his father ran out
the great gate of the castle, the giant was hot on their
heels. He put out a great fist to grab them, but the
two clung fast to the harp. With its powerful wings
it flew and dragged them along to the beanstalk. Down
they climbed in a hurry. The giant came right down
after them. Down he came, snorting and raging; but,
as soon as Jack and his father were safely on the ground,
Jack called for a hatchet. The giant was almost on
them when the lad laid his hatchet straight to the
root of the magic beanstalk. No sooner had he done
so than the whole beanstalk shriveled up, the giant
fell smack to the earth and burst like a monstrous bubble.
Then Jack and his mother and father fell into each
other's arms and rejoiced to be together once more. As
for the giant's wife in the land beyond the beanstalk,
she, without doubt, was glad to be freed from the wicked
curelty of such a terrific bully.

Dick Whittington and His Cat

AN ENGLISH LEGEND

ALONG time ago, in the reign of King Edward III, there lived in England a boy called Dick Whittington. Dick had no father or mother and he was very poor. Often he had nothing to eat and he was happy, indeed, when the poor people in the village could spare him a crust of bread or a few potatoes.

Now, these good country folk forever talked about London. Not one of them had really been there, but they seemed to know all about it just the same. Some said that all the people who lived in London were fine gentlemen and ladies, and that there was singing and music there all day long. Others said that nobody was ever hungry there, and the streets were all paved with gold.

Dick listened eagerly to these stories, and began to wish with all his heart that he could visit that wonderful city. One day, there came dashing up to the village inn a great wagon drawn by eight horses — all with bells on their heads. Dick said to himself, at once, that this wagon must be going to the fine city of London.

When the driver was ready to start off again, the lad ran up to him and asked if he might not walk by the side of the wagon. Thinking that such a ragged boy could not be worse off than he was at present, the driver told him that he might do as he liked. So off started Dick with the wagon. It was a long walk for a boy, but Dick trudged sturdily on until at last he came to the great, big city of London. In such a hurry was he to see the wonderful sights that he ran off as soon as he got there, forgetting altogether to thank the good-natured driver. Up one street and down another he went, trying to find those marvelous streets that were paved with gold.

"Now," he thought to himself, "if I could only find those golden streets, I could break a little bit off the pavement and buy everything I need."

He ran and ran and ran till he was so tired he could go no farther, but in all the streets there was only dirt and not a sign of gold. At last, as night was falling, he sat down in a dark corner and cried himself to sleep. When he awoke, it was morning, and he was very hungry. Having nothing whatever to eat and no money with which to buy food, he walked from one street to another, begging for just a penny from the people whom he met.

"Go to work, you idle fellow," cried some of these; and the rest passed him by without even looking at him.

By and by, having grown so hungry and tired he could go no farther, he lay down by the door of a very fine house.

"If only I knew how to find work!" he sobbed.

"What are you doing there, you little beggar?" It was the cook of the house calling to him. "Get away quick, or I'll throw my panful of dishwater over you! It's hot enough to make you jump!"

But just at that moment, the master of the house, a man named Mr. Fitzwarren, happened to be coming home to dinner. When he saw the ragged little fellow lying so forlorn at his door, he said to him very kindly:

"Well, well, my lad! Why are you lying there? You seem old enough to work. Can it be you are lazy?"

"No, indeed!" cried Dick. "I'd work with all my heart, if I could find anything to do. But I don't know a soul in London, and I haven't eaten for so long!"

"Poor little fellow!" said Mr. Fitzwarren. "Come into the house and I'll see what I can do for you."

So the merchant took the lad into his home. He ordered the cook to give him some dinner and then find him some sort of work. Thus it was that Dick was well-settled in the Fitzwarren house where he would have lived very happily, if it had not been for the cook.

"You are under my orders now!" she would cry. "Stand around there! Clean the spit! Make the fires! Wash these dishes! Bring in the wood! And do it all quickly or . . ." And she would shake her ladle, box his ears, or flourish her broomstick over his shoulders.

At last, however, little Mistress Alice Fitzwarren, daughter of the merchant, chanced to see how the lad was treated and she told the cook she would be turned

away at once if she did not use him more kindly. After that, Dick had an easier time; but there was still something else that troubled him.

His bed was in a garret at the top of the house, and there were so many holes in the floor and walls that, every night, great numbers of rats and mice came in. They raced back and forth over Dick, and made his room so unpleasant that he did not know what to do. One day he earned a penny from a gentleman for cleaning his shoes, and he said to himself that the best use he could make of the money would be to buy a cat with it. The very next morning he met a girl with a cat in her arms.

"I'll give you a penny for that cat," he said.

"Well and good!" the girl answered. "You may have her, and you'll find mice don't stay where she is."

So Dick hid his cat in the garret, and, every day, he was careful to save a part of his dinner and carry it up to her. Soon she had driven all the rats and mice away, so Dick slept soundly every night.

Not long after this, a ship that belonged to Mr. Fitzwarren was loaded and made ready to start on a voyage to a far-off land across the sea. Now, Mr. Fitzwarren always gave his servants the chance to send out in his

ships something of their own, in the hopes of trading it
at a good profit for them; so he called his servants together and asked what each would like to venture on this
vessel. Everyone had something to send—everyone, that
is, but Dick. As he had neither money nor goods, he did
not join the servants in the parlor. Little Mistress Alice
guessed at once why he did not come.

"Father," she said, "surely
Dick should have a chance
with the others. Here is some
money from my own purse
that you may take for him."

But Mr. Fitzwarren answered, "No, my child! He must
send something of his own."
Then he called Dick and said,
"What are you going to venture on the ship, my lad?"

"I have nothing in the
world to send," answered
Dick, "nothing, but a cat."

"If you have a cat, fetch
her and let her go," said Mr.
Fitzwarren. "Who knows but
that she may be traded for
some good profit to you!"

So Dick brought poor Puss
with tears in his eyes.

He carried her to the ship himself and gave her to the Captain with many farewell squeezes. Everybody laughed at the thought of making a fortune by trading nothing but a cat—everybody, that is, except Mistress Alice, and she was sorry for Dick and tried to comfort him.

After that, though Dick worked as faithfully as ever, the cook grew more and more ill-tempered. She made fun of him, too, for sending his cat to sea.

"Perhaps your puss," she would say, "will sell for money enough to buy a stick to beat you!"

At last Dick could no longer bear the hard work and the harsh treatment; so he made up his mind to leave the place. He packed up his few poor belongings and very, very early on All-hallows Day, he started away from the house. He walked as far as Holloway, and there he sat

down to rest for a moment on a stone. But as he sat there, sadly wondering which road he should take, he suddenly heard the six great bells on Bow Church in the distance, ringing out a merry chime. What was it they seemed to say? How strange! What was it they said? That distant chime seemed to say:

"Turn again, Whittington,
Thrice Lord Mayor of London!
Turn again, Whittington,
Thrice Lord Mayor of London!"

"Lord Mayor of London!" cried Dick. "Could I be Lord Mayor of London? If I thought I could, that would be worth working for! 'Turn again,' the bells said. Yes, that's just what I'll do. I'll turn back to my work. Let the old cook cuff and scold me as she pleases! I've got something to work for! To be Lord Mayor of London!"

And Dick went back to his work as quickly as he could. Happily, he reached the kitchen and was already at work before the cook came downstairs. And the stone on which he sat and made that important decision is to this very day called "Whittington's Stone."

Meantime Mistress Puss was journeying over the sea in Mr. Fitzwarren's ship. The ship made a very long voyage; and, at last, it was driven by the winds up on the coast of Africa. The Moors, who lived in those parts had never seen white men before, and they came in great crowds to stare at the pale faces of the strangers. Soon they were buying the fine things with which the ship was loaded. Seeing this, the Captain sent samples of his best wares to the king of the country, which was Barbary. It was not long after this before the king sent for the Captain to come and visit the palace.

As soon as the Captain arrived, he was shown at once into a splendid chamber and invited to seat himself on a rich and beautiful carpet all flowered with silver and gold.

The King and Queen sat in state at the upper end of the room, and no sooner was all in readiness than a number of servants came in bearing steaming dishes of food. But scarcely had they set the dishes down upon the table, when an army of rats and mice rushed pellmell into the room and devoured all the food in a twinkling. The Captain wondered greatly. "Is it not most unpleasant," he asked, "to have so many rats and mice about the palace? And do you do nothing at all to drive them away?"

"Alas!" the King answered. "It is, indeed, most unpleasant, but we have tried in vain to drive the mice and rats away. I would give half my treasure to be rid of them."

At that an idea flashed suddenly into the Captain's mind! Dick Whittington's cat! The Captain cried out to the King that he had a little creature on his ship which would make short work of the pests.

The King was overjoyed. "Bring her here to me," he said. "If she will do what you say, I will load your ship with gold in exchange for such a treasure!"

"I do not like to part with her, but to oblige your Majesty, I will fetch her," said the Captain.

"Do! Ah, do!" cried the Queen.

So the Captain went down to the ship, while another dinner was being made ready in the palace. He took Puss in his arms and returned to the King, just in time to see a second army of rats rush out on the newly-brought food. Seeing those rats and mice, Puss was out of the Captain's arms and in among her foes in an instant. How she made

after the creatures! And how they scampered away! Soon there was not one single mouse or rat left on the table!

The King cried out in his joy, and the Queen desired that the pretty little creature which had served them all so well, should be brought for her to look at. "Pussy, pussy, pussy!" called the Captain, and Mistress Puss came bounding in a very graceful way. The Captain lifted her up to put her on the Queen's lap, but the Queen drew back at first and was half-afraid to touch her. But when she saw how the Captain stroked the pretty, soft fur, and called "Pussy, pussy, pussy!" she ventured to stroke her, too. "Putty, putty, putty!" she called for that was all she could say, as she had not learned to speak English. And, when once she had the cat on her lap, the Queen would not have parted with her for all the gold in Barbary.

So the King made a bargain with the Captain to buy all the goods on the ship; but, for Dick Whittington's cat, he paid ten times as much as for all the goods put together. Then the Captain took leave of the King and Queen of Barbary, and set sail again for England.

One morning, some months later, Mr. Fitzwarren in his counting-house was counting out his money, when he heard someone tap on the door.

"Who's there?" he demanded.

'A friend," the answer came. "A friend, with news of your good ship 'Unicorn.' "

Mr. Fitzwarren hastened to open the door at once and there stood the Captain before him, with a bill-of-lading in one hand and a box of jewels in the other. So full of joy was the merchant at learning of the safe return of his ship, that he most devoutly thanked Heaven for sending him such good fortune.

The first story the Captain told was about Mistress Puss and her fate; and he showed his master all the rich payment the King had made in exchange for poor Dick's cat. As soon as Mr. Fitzwarren heard this remarkable tale, he called out loudly to his servants:

"Go send him in, and tell him of his fame;
Pray call him *Mr. Whittington* by name!"

Dick was scouring pots for the cook when word was brought to him that he was summoned to the counting-house to go before his master.

"To the counting-house! I can't go! I'm too dirty!" cried Dick in dismay. But he was bidden to go as he was, in his working clothes, all the same.

No sooner had he appeared than Mr. Fitzwarren addressed him as Mr. Whittington and he ordered a chair to be set for him. Then the lad thought surely his master and the men must be poking fun at him.

"Don't poke fun at a simple lad! Let me go back to work," said he.

"Mr. Whittington," said Mr. Fitzwarren, "no one is poking fun at you. This is what has happened. The Captain has sold your cat to the King of Barbary and, in return for her, he has brought you more riches than all I have put together."

Then he bade his men open the treasure chest and show Dick what was in it. The poor boy could not believe his eyes. He begged his master to take at least a part of the treasure, but Mr. Fitzwarren said, "No, it is all your own. I feel sure you will use it well."

Next Dick asked Mistress Alice to take some of the jewels, but she, too, said no and thanked him.

"Your good fortune makes me happy, and you've deserved it all!" she said.

So Dick made presents to the Captain, the sailors, and the servants in Mr. Fitzwarren's household. And when his face was washed, and his hair was curled, and he was dressed in a fine suit of clothes, he appeared as handsome a youth as one could wish to see.

Some years after this, there was a splendid wedding at one of the beautiful churches in London. Mistress Alice became the wife of Mr. Richard Whittington. And the lord mayor was there and the great judges and the sheriffs and many more besides. But Richard Whittington, in spite of his great fortune, worked on as diligently as ever. He was first a successful merchant, then sheriff of the city, and thrice lord mayor of London. King Henry V bestowed upon him the honor of knighthood, and he became Sir Richard Whittington. Thus, by going back to his work, no matter how hard he found it, he proved the words of the great bells of Bow to be true when they called him "Whittington, thrice Lord Mayor of London."

Jamie Watt and the Tea Kettle

Jamie Watt, a little Scotch boy, sat by the great fireplace in his grandmother's kitchen. Above the rosy flames there hung an old-fashioned tea kettle.

Jamie had been whittling a piece of wood and making a cart with wheels, but now he dropped his work in his lap. Something had happened to the tea kettle that caught his eye, and he began to watch it closely, for he never let anything strange pass by without finding out the reason for it. The water in the kettle had begun to boil and a little white column of steam was puffing out from its spout. Pretty soon, S-s-s! S-s-s! Piff! Piff! Piff! the lid of the tea kettle began to rattle. S-s-s! S-s-s! Piff! Piff! Piff! something lifted the lid right up in the air!

"O Grandma! Grandma!" cried the boy in great excitement. "What is there inside of your tea kettle?"

Grandma was busy laying the table for supper.

"Nothing but water, Jamie!" she answered.

S-s-s! S-s-s! Piff! Piff! Piff! Up popped the lid again. The boy watched it, breathless with interest.

"But, Grandma, there must be something inside the kettle," he insisted. "See! Something keeps lifting the lid!"

"Ho, ho!" laughed his grandmother. "Perhaps it's a brownie or a pixie you're thinking is in the kettle! No, no! It's only the steam that does the lifting! See clouds of it are puffing out all around the lid."

Now Jamie wasn't thinking at all that it was a brownie or a pixie that was in the kettle. But he was thinking

45

that he wanted very much to know what this thing called steam was, that had so much strength and power. Carefully he leaned over and lifted the lid to look inside. Nothing at all could he see but boiling, bubbling water.

"Grandma," he asked, "where does the steam come from? How did it get into the kettle?"

Grandma was used to his questions; he was always wondering about things.

"Why, dearie," she answered, "steam always rises from water whenever water boils."

The boy stood studying the kettle for a little longer, then he sat down again, and while he was thinking he began absent-mindedly spinning the wheels on the little cart he was making. At last he burst out:

"Grandma, if the steam in that kettle is strong enough to lift the lid, why couldn't steam from a great deal more water lift much heavier things? Why—why couldn't it push wheels around?"

"Push wheels around!" Grandma did not even try to answer so absurd a question. Jamie had strange and idle dreams, she thought, and she wished he would spend his time thinking of something more useful than pushing wheels around with steam. But Jamie never left off wondering about the steam just the same, nor was his wondering so idle and useless as his grandmother supposed.

"That steam has the strength of a giant," he used to say to himself. "If I could only find out how to make use of it, it would not only lift heavy weights, but it would make machinery go, and do all sorts of work for men."

So Jamie went on studying and working as he grew to be a man. Many times he made experiments with steam engines and his engines failed to go, but he always learned something new from each failure. Other people thought him foolish and laughed at him.

"Ho, ho! Jamie Watt is going to harness up the clouds that puff out of his granny's tea kettle and make them do the work of a giant!" they would jeer. But in spite of all this, Jamie worked on year after year until at last he did indeed make what no one had thought he could—a steam engine that was a success. And that was the little Scotch boy's great gift to the world.

It was Jamie's engine that made possible the engines that draw trains, push steamboats and turn machinery. Men had lived for thousands of years beside that great giant, Steam, and yet not one of them ever learned how to harness it and make its mighty power of service to man, till one small boy began to wonder how it lifted the lid off the tea kettle in his granny's kitchen.

The Boyhood of Robert Fulton

ROBERT FULTON had more ideas than any other boy in Lancaster, Pennsylvania. He was always designing remarkable things to supply his own boyish wants, the needs of his mother and his friends. Sometimes he was late to school and narrowly escaped a trouncing from the schoolmaster's stout birch rod; but the schoolmaster, in his secret heart, believed the world would yet hear from this queer little urchin he often threatened to beat.

When the Fourth of July drew near in 1778, Robert—then thirteen years old—planned, with the other boys, a wonderful celebration in honor of the second anniversary of the Declaration of Independence. The men of the town were still fighting in the American Revolution; and the boys, in their bubbling devotion to the cause of liberty, planned to light the whole city splendidly with candles. On the first of July, however, the city council decreed that, in such trying times, people must save all they could to give for the use of the army. And, since tallow for candles was scarce, they ordered that no one should light a candle to celebrate the Fourth.

A sad blow that for the boys! They stood before the signboard announcing this order of the council, their faces long and sober. Robert Fulton alone wasted no time in regrets. He stood for a few moments lost in thought, then he hurried home and buried himself for a time in a book. Afterwards he went to the brushmakers and exchanged his candles for gunpowder. At a second shop, he bought cardboard.

"What are you going to do with cardboard?" asked the clerk in the second shop.

"We are forbidden to light the streets with candles," the boy answered eagerly, "so I'm going to light the sky with rockets!"

"Light the sky! Why, that's impossible!" The man laughed heartily for fireworks were at that time almost unknown in America, though they had long been used in China.

"Impossible!" cried the boy. "Nothing is impossible!" And he marched off home with his purchases.

When darkness came on the Fourth, the boys gathered in the square and built a gigantic bonfire. Their shouts and the leaping of the flames summoned everyone to the square. A row of cardboard cylinders attached to sticks, lay on the grass. Under Robert's direction the boys had made these cylinders, taking the utmost care to have them the right length and thickness, with the stick just the proper length in proportion to the size of the cylinders. The rockets were filled with gunpowder and a number of little balls, made by Robert himself out of such stuff as he knew would produce colored fire. All this Robert had carefully worked out from the general description in his book.

The boys set off the rockets. A loud report, then a streak of fire shot hissing up in the air to burst gloriously in the sky with a great bouquet of stars!

Everyone thanked Robert Fulton, who had worked out that celebration; and the boys, themselves, felt that rockets proved to be better than candles as a means of venting their spirits and celebrating the Fourth. After this, Robert continued experimenting with things and haunting the factories where arms were made for the Continental Army. He had so many ideas, he drew his plans so well, that he often gave older workmen valuable suggestions.

Always and eternally he was experimenting. Sometimes he worked quite mysteriously on problems he would not discuss with his fellows. Once, he continued day after day to go to the druggist's for quicksilver. Great was the curiosity to know what he could be doing with that strange metal that acts as if bewitched. No one ever found out. He kept it a secret, but his comrades thenceforth nicknamed him "Quicksilver Bob."

In 1779, when Robert was fourteen, he met, among the factory youths, a lad who rejoiced in the name of Christopher Gumpf. Now Christopher liked to fish and he kept an old flatboat padlocked to a tree on the banks of the Conestoga Creek. On holidays, he and Robert would set out with bait and lunch for a glorious day upstream. The flatboat was pushed by a pole, and the boys took turns at poling. But it was a tedious task to push the clumsy, old scow for any distance upstream, so Robert's active mind began to work on the problem of how men could more easily make a boat move through the water. While he was thinking of this, he went to visit an aunt

and at her home in New Britain, he entertained himself by making a model of a boat to be propelled by paddles at the sides. The model was too large for Robert to carry home, so he left it in his aunt's attic. Little did she guess, when she found the strange contraption, that in after years it would be her most cherished possession!

Robert confided to Christopher his plan for moving a boat by means of paddle wheels; so, after much secret hammering in the woods by the river, the lads made a set of side paddles, to move their old friend, the scow. The paddle wheels were joined by a bar and worked by a crank. One boy, standing in the center of the boat, could turn the crank, which turned the bar, which turned the paddle wheels, which made the boat go forward!

When the contrivance was finished, Christopher himself could hardly believe it would work; but Robert, with no doubts at all, stepped into the boat, laid hold of the crank and turned it. Off went the scow gliding along upstream.

For a day of delighted triumph, the boys enjoyed their success and the astonished faces of the spectators who stopped, open-mouthed, to watch them from the banks of the Conestoga. Very little effort now sent the boat a long distance. It was much easier and faster than the old-fashioned method of poling.

So it was in the little town of Lancaster, Pennsylvania, on the Conestoga Creek, with only a few people to watch his queer contrivance, little dreaming what it would lead to, that Robert Fulton, as a boy, began to plan easier ways to make boats move in the water.

Years later, in place of these few astonished farmers lining a creek to see a paddle-wheeled scow, crowds of people were to line the banks of the Hudson River, in New York, to see Robert Fulton's Clermont, the first successful steamboat ever launched.

Steaming its way upstream, the Clermont puffed out its message to all the watching world that the day of sailboats was ended. It ushered in the day of steamboats, great steam engines and machines. For Robert Fulton had harnessed that powerful giant, Steam, whose possibilities for moving things Jamie Watt had discovered. He had made it move a great boat.

And the inventor of the Clermont, the boat that changed the whole method of traveling by water, was that same Robert Fulton, who had proclaimed as a boy, when he wanted to make skyrockets, that "nothing is impossible."

THE SWITCH YARD*

John Curtis Underwood

Out of the glimmer of arc lights and spaces of shade,
Far on the frontier the city has won from the dark,
Rails in the moonlight in ribbons of silver are laid;
Eyes that are watchful the loom of the switch yard shall mark;
Ears that are keen to its music shall hark.

Red, green, and gold are the signals that mark the design,
Black is the ground where the work of the weaver is spread,
Bright in the night is the glittering length of the line,
Swiftly and strongly and surely the shuttles are sped,
Bringing and braiding and breaking the thread.

Clicking of switches and resonant rolling of wheels
Mix in the midnight with stifled escape of steam.
Down the long siding a shadowed shape silently steals;
Sudden it checks; and the grind of the brakes is a scream,
The sound of a rent in the stuff of the dream.

*Used by permission of the publishers, G. P. Putnam's Sons.

53

The Pony Engine and the Pacific Express*

WILLIAM DEAN HOWELLS

CHRISTMAS EVE, after the children had hung up their stockings and got all ready for St. Nick, they climbed up on the papa's lap to kiss him goodnight, and when they both got their arms round his neck, they said they were not going to bed till he told them a Christmas story. Then he saw that he would have to mind, for they were awfully severe with him, and always made him do exactly what they told him; it was the way they had brought him up. He tried his best to get out of it for awhile; but, after they had shaken him first this side and then that side, and pulled him backward and forward till he did not know where he was, he began to think perhaps he had better begin. The first thing he said, after he opened his eyes and made believe he had been asleep, or something, was, "Well, where did I leave off?" And that made them just perfectly boiling, for they understood his tricks, and they knew he was trying to pretend he had told part of the story already. They said he had not left off anywhere because he had not commenced, and he saw it was no use. So he commenced:

*Abridged from the story in *Christmas Every Day and Other Stories*. Copyright by Harper & Brothers.

"Once there was a little Pony Engine that used to play round the Fitchburg Depot on the sidetracks, and sleep in among the big locomotives in the carhouse—"

The little girl lifted her head from the papa's shoulder, where she had dropped it. "Is it a sad story, Papa?"

"How is it going to end?" asked the boy.

"Well, it's got a moral," said the papa.

. "Oh, all right, if it's got a moral," said the children; they had a good deal of fun with morals the papa put to his stories. The papa said, "Now every time you stop me, I shall have to begin all over again." But he saw that this was not going to spite them any, so he went on: "One of the locomotives was its mother, and she had got hurt once in a big smashup, so that she couldn't run long trips anymore. But she could work round the depot, and pull empty cars in and out, and shunt them off on the sidetracks, and she was so anxious to be useful that all the other engines respected her and they were very kind to the little Pony Engine on her account, though it was always getting in the way and under their wheels.

They all knew it was an orphan; for, before its mother got hurt, its father went through a bridge one dark night into an arm of the sea and was never heard of again. The old mother locomotive used to say that it would never have happened if she had been there; but, poor dear No. 236 was always so venturesome, and she had warned him against that very bridge time and again. Then she would whistle so dolefully and sigh with her airbrakes enough to make anybody cry. You see they used to be a very happy family when they were all to-gether, before the papa locomotive got drowned. He was very fond of the little Pony Engine, and told it stories at night after they got into the carhouse, at the end of some of his long runs. It would get up on his cowcatcher, and lean its chimney up against his, and listen till it fell asleep. Then he would put it softly down, and be off again in the morning before it was awake. The little Pony Engine could just remember him; it was awfully proud of its papa."

The boy lifted his head and looked at the little girl, who suddenly hid her face in the papa's other shoulder. "Well, I declare, Papa, she was putting up her lip."

"It wasn't any such thing!" said the little girl. "And I don't care! So!" and then she sobbed.

"Now, never you mind," said the papa to the boy. "You'll be putting up *your* lip before I'm through. Well, and then she used to caution the little Pony Engine against getting in the way of the big locomotives, and told it to keep close round after her and try to do all it could to learn about shifting empty cars. You see, she knew how ambitious the little Pony Engine was, and how it wasn't contented a bit just to grow up in the pony-engine business, and be tied down to the depot all its days. Once she happened to tell it that, if it was good and always did what it was bid, perhaps a cowcatcher would grow on it some day and then it could be a passenger locomotive."

"I don't think she ought to have deceived it, Papa," said the boy. "But it should have known that if it was a Pony Engine, it never could have a cowcatcher."

"Couldn't it?" asked the little girl, gently.

"No, they're kind of mooley."

The little girl asked the papa. "What makes Pony Engines mooley?" for she did not choose to be told by her brother; he was only two years older than she was, anyway.

"Well, it's pretty hard to say. You see, when a locomotive is first hatched—"

"Oh, are they hatched, Papa?" asked the boy. "Well, we'll call it hatched," said the papa; but they knew he was just funning. "They're about the size of teakettles at first; and it's a chance whether they will have cowcatchers or not!

"The thing that the little Pony Engine wanted to be, the most in this world, was the locomotive of the Pacific Express. That starts out every afternoon at three, you know. It intended to apply for the place as soon as its cowcatcher was grown, and it was always trying to attract the locomotive's attention, backing and filling on the track alongside of the train; and, once, it raced it a little piece and beat it, before the Express locomotive was under way, and almost got in front of it on a switch. My, but its mother was scared! She just yelled to it with her whistle; and that night she sent it to sleep without a particle of coal or water in its tender. But the little Pony Engine didn't care. It has beaten the Pacific Express in a hundred yards, and what was to hinder it from beating it as long as it chose?

"Well, one dark, snowy, blowy afternoon, when his mother was off pushing some empty coal cars up past the Know-Nothing crossing beyond Charlestown, he got on the track in front of the Express; and, when he heard the conductor say 'All aboard,' and the starting gong struck and the brakeman leaned out and waved to the engineer, he darted off like lightning. He had his steam up, and he just scuttled.

"Well, he was so excited for awhile that he couldn't tell whether the Express was gaining on him or not; but after twenty or thirty miles, he thought he heard it pretty near. Of course the Express locomotive was drawing a heavy train of cars, and it had to make a stop or two—so the Pony Engine did really gain on it a little; and, when it began to be scared, it gained a good deal. But the first place where it began to feel sorry and to want its

mother, was in Hoosac Tunnel. It never was in a tunnel before, and it seemed as it if would never get out. It kept thinking—what if the Pacific Express was to run over it there in the dark, and its mother off there at the Fitchburg Depot, in Boston, looking for it among the sidetracks? It gave a perfect shriek; and, just then, it shot out of the tunnel. There were a lot of locomotives loafing around there at North Adams, and one of them shouted out to it as it flew by, 'What's your hurry, little one?' and it just screamed back, 'Pacific Express!' and never stopped to explain. They talked in locomotive language—"

"Oh, what did it sound like?" the boy asked.

"Well, pretty queer; I'll tell you some day. It knew it had no time to fool away; and all through the long, dark night, whenever a locomotive hailed it, it just screamed, 'Pacific Express!' and kept on. And the Express kept gaining on it. Some of the locomotives wanted to stop it, but they decided they had better not get in its way; and so it whizzed along across New York State, and Ohio, and Indiana, till it got to Chicago. And the Express kept gaining on it. By that time, it was so hoarse it could hardly whisper; but it kept saying, 'Pacific Express! Pacific Express!' and it kept right on till it reached the Mississippi River. There it found a long train of cars before it on the bridge. It couldn't wait, so it slipped down to the edge of the river, jumped across, and then scrambled up the embankment to the track again."

"Papa!" said the little girl, warningly.

"Truly it did," said the papa. "Well, after that, it had a little rest for the Express had to wait for the freight train to get off the bridge, and the Pony Engine stopped at the first station for a drink of water and a mouthful of coal, and then it flew ahead. And the Express kept gaining on it. On the plains it was chased by a pack of prairie wolves, but it left them far behind; and the antelopes were scared half to death. But the worst of it was when the nightmare got after it."

"The nightmare? Goodness!" said the boy. "What's it like?"

"Well, it has only one leg, to begin with—wheel, I mean. And it has four cowcatchers and four headlights and two boilers and eight whistles, and it just goes whirling and screaming along. Of course, it wobbles awfully; and as it's only got one wheel, it has to keep skipping from one track to the other."

"I should think it would run on the crossties," said the boy.

"Oh, very well, then," said the papa, "if you know so much more about it than I do! Who's telling this story, anyway? Now I shall have to go back to the beginning. Once, there was a little Pony En—"

They both put their hands over his mouth and just fairly begged him to go on, and at last he did. "Well, it got away from the nightmare about morning, but not till the nightmare had bitten a large piece out of its tender, and then it braced up for the home stretch. It thought that if it could once beat the Express to the Sierras, it could keep the start the rest of the way, for it could get over the mountains quicker than the Express could, and it might be in San Francisco before the Express got to Sacramento. The Express kept gaining on it. But it just zipped along the upper edge of Kansas and the lower edge of Nebraska, and on through Colorado, and Utah, and Nevada. And, when it got to the Sierras, it just stopped a little and went over them like a goat. It did, truly. Just doubled up its fore wheels under it and jumped. And the Express kept gaining on it. By this time it couldn't say 'Pacific Express' any more, and it didn't try. It just said 'Express! Express!' and then ''Press! 'Press!' and then ''Ess! 'Ess!' and pretty soon only ''Ss! 'Ss!' And the Express kept gaining on it. Before they reached San Francisco, the Express locomotive's cowcatcher was almost touching the Pony Engine's tender.

It gave one howl of anguish as it felt the Express locomotive's hot breath on the place where the nightmare had bitten the piece out, and tore through the end of the San Francisco depot, and plunged into the Pacific Ocean, and was never seen again.

"There, now," said the papa, "that's all. Go to bed."

The boy cleared his throat. "What is the moral, Papa?" he asked, huskily.

"Children, obey your parents," said the papa.

The boy thought awhile. "Well, I don't see what it had to do with Christmas, anyway."

"Why, it was Christmas Eve when the Pony Engine started from Boston, and Christmas afternoon when it reached San Francisco."

"Ho!" said the boy. "No locomotive could get across the continent in a day and a night."

"Well, perhaps it was a year. Maybe it was the *next* Christmas after that when it got to San Francisco."

The papa started to run out of the room, and both of the children ran after him, to pound him. When they were in bed the boy called to the papa, "Well, anyway, I didn't put up my lip."

CASEY JONES*

A Song of the Railroad Men

COME all you fellows, for I want you to hear
The story told of a brave engineer.
Casey Jones was the fellow's name,
On a big eight-wheeler of a mighty fame.

Caller called Casey 'bout half past four,
And he kissed his wife at the station door;
Climbed to the cab with his orders in his hand;
Said, "Boys, this is my trip to the Holy Land."

The rain had been coming down for five or six weeks.
The railroad track was like the bed of a creek.
They slowed the train down to a thirty-mile gait,
Made the south-bound mail some eight hours late.

Fireman says, "Casey, you're running too fast.
You ran the block signal, last station you passed."
Casey says, "Yes, but we'll make it though,
For she steams a lot better than I ever know."

Casey says, "Fireman, don't you fret,
Keep knockin' at the fire door, don't give up yet!
I'm goin' to run this train till she leaves the rail,
Or make it on time with the south-bound mail!"

*This song of the railroad men, first sung by a crew in a roundhouse, depicted in true ballad style the dangers and tragedies of early railroading. When Casey Jones was killed in a wreck near Memphis, more verses were added with Casey as the hero.

He pulled back the throttle for Reno Hill,
The whistle for the crossing was awful shrill,
The switchman knew by the engine's moans
That the man at the throttle was Casey Jones

He rounded the curve within a mile of the place,
Old No. 4 stared him right in the face,
He turned to his fireman said, "Boy, you'd better jump
'Cause there's two locomotives that are going to bump!"

Poor Casey Jones was sure all right,
He stuck to his duty day and night.
Fireman jumped off, but Casey stayed on—
A good engineer, but he's dead and gone.

Headaches and heartaches and all kinds of pain
Are never apart from a railroad train.
Stories of brave men, noble and grand
Belong to the life of a railroad man.

Wilbur Wright and Orville Wright*

Rosemary and Stephen Vincent Benét

SAID Orville Wright to Wilbur Wright,
  "These birds are very trying.
I'm sick of hearing them cheep-cheep
About the fun of flying.
A bird has feathers, it is true.
That much I freely grant.
But, must that stop us, W?"
Said Wilbur Wright, "It shan't."
And so they built a glider, first,
And then they built another.
—There never were two brothers more
Devoted to each other.
They ran a dusty little shop
For bicycle-repairing,
And bought each other soda-pop
and praised each other's daring.
They glided here, they glided there,
They sometimes skinned their noses.
—For learning how to rule the air
Was not a bed of roses—

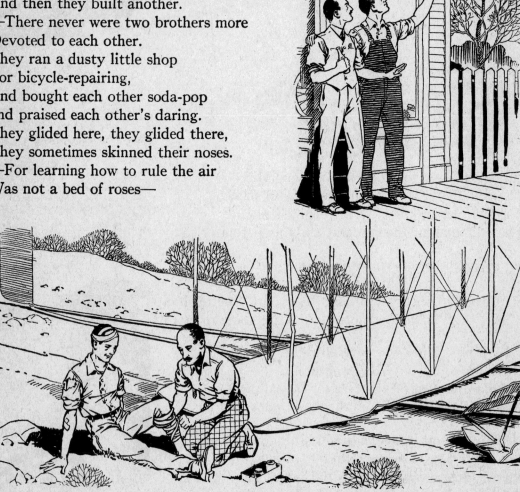

*From *A Book of Americans*, published by Farrar & Rinehart, Inc., copyright, 1933, by Rosemary and Stephen Vincent Benét.

But each would murmur, afterward,
While patching up his bro.
"Are we discouraged, W?"
"Of course we are not, O!"
And finally, at Kitty Hawk
In Nineteen-Three (let's cheer it!)
The first real airplane really flew
With Orville there to steer it!
—And kingdoms may forget their kings
And dogs forget their bites,
But, not till Man forgets his wings,
Will men forget the Wrights.

Getting their early knowledge of mechanics in a bicycle repair shop, Orville and Wilbur Wright produced the first airplane of practical usefulness. After spending years experimenting, they made their first successful flight in 1903, at Kitty Hawk.

A Little Boy in Paris*

LITTLE Anatole lived in a house on a sleepy old quay near the river Seine, in Paris. From his window he could look out on the great, gray palace of the Louvre, the tall towers of Notre Dame, and all the beauty of old Paris with its jewels of carven stone. Below him flowed the river, spanned by nobly arching bridges. By day, it mirrored the sky and bore boats on its bosom; by night, it decked itself with jewels and sparkling flowers of light.

Anatole's greatest pleasure in life was going for walks in the city. Taking his hand in hers, his mother would lead him along the streets and take him into the shops. There was nothing in all the world Anatole loved like those shops. They seemed to him full of treasures and the sight of the rich silks and velvets, embroideries, flowers, and feathers filled his heart with delight.

There was the tailor shop and the grocer shop and best of all, the house of Debeauve and Gallais, chocolate makers

*The story of Jacques Anatole Thibault (1844-1924), called Anatole France, is taken from autobiographical materia. in *My Friend's Book*, *Little Pierre Noziere*, and *The Bloom of Life*. See Vol. II, p. 71, for a story by Anatole France.

to the Kings of France. Whenever Anatole went into that chocolate shop, he felt as though he were entering a fairy palace. The windows were high and arched. There were glass cabinets and long mirrors about, and the far end of the room was rounded like a little temple with the semicircular counter following the curve of the room. There sat pretty young ladies, some busy covering the chocolates with shiny silver paper while others wrapped the cakes, two at a time, in white-paper wrappers with pictures on them.

When Anatole's mother had completed her purchases, an older woman, who sat at the counter, would take a chocolate drop from a crystal bowl beside her and give it to Anatole. And this gift, more than anything else, made him love and admire the shop of Messrs. Debeauve and Gallais, chocolate makers to the Kings of France.

Now Anatole was an only child and he played a great deal by himself. One day, he made up his mind that he must do something remarkable to make his name known in the world. Often his mother read him stories of the saints, and, when he heard how St. Antony and St. Jerome went out into the desert to live among lions and tigers, he decided that he would do likewise. The very next day he would go and live at the zoo! There were plenty of lions and tigers there, and there was a hill with a little hut on it. He could live there alone, clad, like St. Paul, the Hermit, in a mantle of palm leaves. He, too, would be great! But, when he told his mother his plan, she only laughed and said, "Anatole, Anatole, what a foolish boy you are!"

Still, Anatole couldn't give up his intention of doing something remarkable and extraordinary in the world. If he couldn't live with lions and tigers, he would just go to the kitchen for he had an idea somehow, that adventures awaited him there. Off he went in a hurry sniffing the savory smell of a rabbit stew that was cooking; but he found the kitchen empty, for Melanie, the cook, having started preparations for lunch, had gone off to do some marketing. The great moment had come for Anatole! He would make a stew, a better stew than Melanie had ever made in her life! He would make such a stew that, when it was served, his father and mother would say, "Whoever made this delicious, delightful, extraordinary stew?" Then he would answer, "I made it, little Anatole!"

So Anatole hid Melanie's stew in the broom closet.

Then he ran and got all the animals from his Noah's Ark. He poured them out, one by one, into a fine, copper saucepan and put them on the fire. Melanie could only cook a rabbit in her stew, but here little Anatole would make a wonderful stew of all the animals in creation from the elephant and the giraffe to the butterfly and the grasshopper. Wouldn't Melanie be surprised! Thinking to find in the saucepan the rabbit she had prepared, she would behold in its stead the lion and the lioness, the he-ass and the she-ass, the elephant and his lady—in a word, all the animals saved from the flood, even Noah and his family, whom Anatole stirred up with the rest!

But the thing did not turn out as Anatole had hoped. He was back in the room with his mother when, all at once, a terrible smell proceeded from the kitchen, a smell wholly unexpected by little Anatole. Coughing and choking, his mother ran to see what had happened; and there was poor old Melanie, gasping for breath in the smoke, her market-basket still on her arm, just taking up the saucepan in which the charred remains of the occupants of the ark were smouldering hideously.

"My stew! My lovely stew!" cried Melanie in despair; and Anatole, who had followed his mother to the kitchen to triumph in his great success, was struck dumb with shame and sorrow. In quavering tones, he told Melanie that her stew was in the broom closet. Anatole was not scolded, but his father, paler than usual, pretended not to see him at lunch and his mother's cheeks were flushed and

red. When Melanie brought in her stew, her eyes, all red from weeping, since it was not fit to eat, Anatole could restrain his sorrow no longer. He rushed to his poor old friend, hugged her with all his might and burst into a flood of tears.

Every day when lunch was over, little Anatole's nurse tied the strings of her white lace bonnet under her chin, put on her little black shawl, and took him out for a walk. Often they walked down the Champs Elysées, that long avenue bordered with shops where men sold gingerbread, sticks of barley sugar, penny whistles, and paper kites. There were goat carriages, too, and merry-go-rounds with wooden horses and a puppet show in its little theatre. But, in spite of all the fun he had, Anatole was always wishing for a little brother. He thought he would be a better boy if only he had a brother. One day he saw a little chimney sweep, his face all grimy with soot, come out of the drawing-room chimney and he asked him to be his brother. The little chimney sweep grinned and willingly agreed. He stayed with Anatole till he had to go home to his mother; then Anatole was left an only child again.

But, when Anatole was big enough to go to school every day, he found a friend in a boy named Fontanet and that was almost as good as having a little brother. With their hoops in their hands and balls in their pockets, the two boys wandered around and looked in shop windows together and neither Anatole's mother nor his nurse had to go with him on his walks anymore.

OBJETS d'ART ANTIQUES

Anatole and Fontanet rambled all day long, about the streets of Paris, their eyes so fixed on shops, that they now and then collided with some dignified old gentleman or perhaps a pastrycook's boy, carefully bearing a hamper of goodies on his head. Often they stayed out until the shadows of evening were beginning to fall, and the windows blazed with lights while all the streets were filled with the laughter, noise, and bustle of people going home.

Best of all, the boys loved to stand before the armorer's shop and peep in at the old swords and lances, the ancient helmets, and suits of armor displayed amid a rich jumble of various objects of art.

"Suppose," said Fontanet, "that we go to the chocolate shop and get some of that silver paper they use for wrapping up chocolates. Then we can each make a fine suit of armor."

That sounded interesting, so the two boys went home and set to work. Anatole labored long until he made a helmet out of the silver paper; but, when he put it on his head and stood proudly looking at Fontanet expecting his approval, Fontanet shook his head. "It's a wizard's cap," he said.

Anatole had to give up. He was not a success as an armorer! To make up for his failure he suggested, "Let's start a museum like the one the armorer has."

Another wonderful plan! But, when the boys came to count up what they could get together to put in a museum, they found they had nothing at all except half a dozen marbles and a dozen tops or so. Meantime, Fontanet, ever since he looked in the armorer's shop, had been dreaming of knightly deeds and all the romance of history.

"I know what let's do," he said. "Let's write a history of France with all the details in fifty volumes!"

The idea enchanted Anatole. To write a history of France, in fifty volumes! The boys began work at once. They decided to begin their history with the story of King Teutobochus. Old Teutobochus, they said, was a giant thirty feet all, a fact which could be proved by measuring the giant's bones, which had just been accidentally discovered and dug up. But now, of course, they must furnish old King Teutobochus with a story equal to the grandeur of his size. That staggered their imagination. They just couldn't think up a story worthy of a giant thirty feet tall who lived long, long ago at the very beginning of time.

"We shall have to skip old Teutobochus," said Fontanet positively.

"But he's too important!" cried Anatole. "We can't write a history of France without beginning with him."

So the history of France, in fifty volumes, stopped short at King Teutobochus. Anatole, however, continued to roam the streets of Paris, in company with his friend. He continued to plan adventures, dream enormous dreams, and lead an interesting life. And, when he grew up, he called himself by the name of the country he loved so well, Anatole France. Then he wrote all the stories he dreamed about in his youth, and children loved the tales he wrote, even though he never told the very interesting history of that remarkable giant, the enormous King Teutobochus.

The Diverting History of John Gilpin

WRITTEN BY WILLIAM COWPER*

Illustrated by Randolph Caldecott

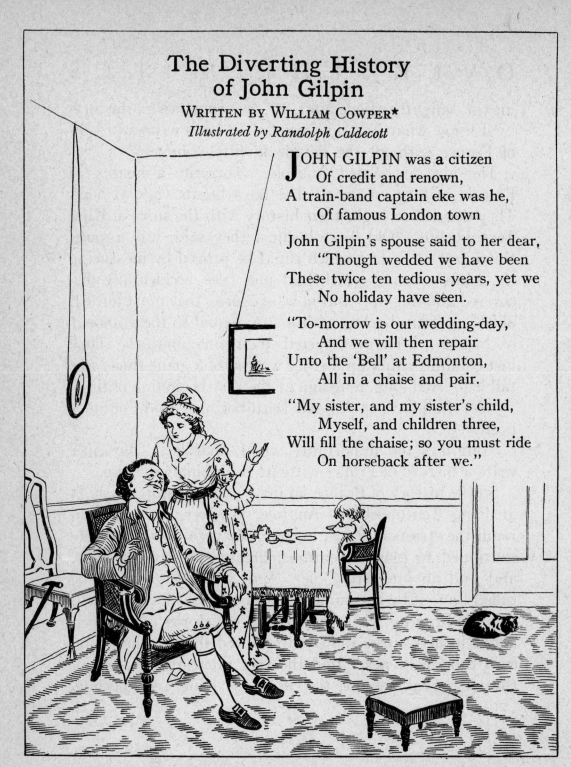

JOHN GILPIN was a citizen
    Of credit and renown,
A train-band captain eke was he,
    Of famous London town

John Gilpin's spouse said to her dear,
    "Though wedded we have been
These twice ten tedious years, yet we
    No holiday have seen.

"To-morrow is our wedding-day,
    And we will then repair
Unto the 'Bell' at Edmonton,
    All in a chaise and pair.

"My sister, and my sister's child,
    Myself, and children three,
Will fill the chaise; so you must ride
    On horseback after we."

*William Cowper (1731-1800), an English poet best known for his long poem, *The Task*, had a rare gift of humor as shown by his membership in the Nonsense Club, in London, and this poem, *John Gilpin*.

He soon replied, "I do admire
  Of womankind but one,
And you are she, my dearest dear,
  Therefore it shall be done.

"I am a linendraper bold,
  As all the world doth know,
And my good friend the calender
  Will lend his horse to go."

Quoth Mrs. Gilpin, "That's well said;
  And for that wine is dear,
We will be furnished with our own,
  Which is both bright and clear."

John Gilpin kissed his loving wife;
  O'erjoyed was he to find,
That though on pleasure she was bent,
  She had a frugal mind.

Books illustrated by Randolph Caldecott which delight children are: *The House That Jack Built, Three Jovial Huntsmen, A Frog, He Would a-Wooing Go, The Great Panjandrum,* and the *Picture Books* Nos. 1 and 2.

The morning came, the chaise was brought,
But yet was not allowed
To drive up to the door, lest all
Should say that she was proud.

So three doors off the chaise was stayed,
Where they did all get in;
Six precious souls, and all agog
To dash through thick and thin.

78

Smack went the whip, round went the wheels,
    Were never folks so glad!
The stones did rattle underneath,
    As if Cheapside were mad.

      John Gilpin at his horse's side
          Seized fast the flowing mane,
      And up he got, in haste to ride,
          But soon came down again;

            For saddletree scarce reached had he,
               His journey to begin,
            When, turning round his head, he saw
               Three customers come in.

                  So down he came; for loss of time,
                     Although it grieved him sore,
                  Yet loss of pence, full well he knew,
                     Would trouble him much more.

'Twas long before the customers
    Were suited to their mind,
When Betty screaming came downstairs,
    "The wine is left behind!"

    "Good lack!" quoth he, "yet bring it me,
        My leathern belt likewise,
    In which I bear my trusty sword
        When I do exercise."

        Now Mistress Gilpin (careful soul!)
            Had two stone bottles found,
        To hold the liquor that she loved,
            And keep it safe and sound.

Each bottle had a curling ear,
    Through which the belt he drew,
And hung a bottle on each side,
    To make his balance true.

    Then over all, that he might be
        Equipped from top to toe,
    His long red cloak, well brushed and neat,
        He manfully did throw.

        Now see him mounted once again
            Upon his nimble steed,
        Full slowly pacing o'er the stones,
            With caution and good heed.

            But finding soon a smoother road
                Beneath his well-shod feet,
            The snorting beast began to trot,
                Which galled him in his seat.

"So, fair and softly!" John he cried,
    But John he cried in vain;
That trot became a gallop soon,
    In spite of curb and rein.

    So stooping down, as needs he must
        Who cannot sit upright,
    He grasped the mane with both his hands,
        And eke with all his might.

        His horse, who never in that sort
            Had handled been before,
        What thing upon his back had got,
            Did wonder more and more.

            Away went Gilpin, neck or nought;
                Away went hat and wig;
            He little dreamt, when he set out,
                Of running such a rig.

The wind did blow, the cloak did fly
     Like streamer long and gay,
Till, loop and button failing both,
     At last it flew away.

          Then might all people well discern
               The bottles he had slung;
          A bottle swinging at each side,
               As hath been said or sung.

                    The dogs did bark, the children screamed,
                         Up flew the windows all;
                    And every soul cried out, "Well done!"
                         As loud as he could bawl.

                         Away went Gilpin—who but he?
                              His fame soon spread around;
                         "He carries weight! He rides a race!
                              'Tis for a thousand pound!"

And still as fast as he drew near,
    'Twas wonderful to view
How in a trice the turnpike-men
    Their gates wide open threw.

And now, as he went bowing down
    His reeking head full low,
        The bottles twain behind his back
    Were shattered at a blow.

Down ran the wine into the road,
    Most piteous to be seen
Which made the horse's flanks to smoke,
    As they had basted been.

But still he seemed to carry weight
   With leathern girdle braced;
For all might see the bottle-necks
   Still dangling at his waist.

Thus all through merry Islington
   These gambols he did play,
Until he came unto the Wash
   Of Edmonton so gay;

And there he threw the wash about
   On both sides of the way,
Just like unto a trundling mop,
   Or a wild goose at play.

At Edmonton his loving wife
    From the balcony spied
Her tender husband, wondering much
    To see how he did ride.

"Stop, stop, John Gilpin!—Here's the house!"
    They all at once did cry;
"The dinner waits, and we are tired";
    Said Gilpin—"So am I!"

But yet his horse was not a whit
    Inclined to tarry there;
For why?—his owner had a house
    Full ten miles off, at Ware.

So like an arrow swift he flew,
    Shot by an archer strong;
So did he fly—which brings me to
    The middle of my song.

Away went Gilpin, out of breath,
    And sore against his will,
Till at his friend the calender's
    His horse at last stood still.

The calender, amazed to see
    His neighbour in such trim,
Laid down his pipe, flew to the gate,
    And thus accosted him:

"What news? what news? your tidings tell;
    Tell me you must and shall—
Say why bareheaded you are come,
    Or why you come at all?"

Now Gilpin had a pleasant wit,
    And loved a timely joke;
And thus unto the calender
    In merry guise he spoke:

"I came because your horse would come;
 And, if I well forebode,
My hat and wig will soon be here,
 They are upon the road."

The calender, right glad to find
 His friend in merry pin,
Returned him not a single word,
 But to the house went in;

Whence straight he came with hat and wig,
 A wig that flowed behind,
A hat not much the worse for wear,
 Each comely in its kind.

He held them up, and in his turn
 Thus showed his ready wit:
"My head is twice as big as yours,
 They therefore needs must fit."

"But let me scrape the dirt away
    That hangs upon your face;
And stop and eat, for well you may
    Be in a hungry case."

Said John, "It is my wedding-day,
    And all the world would stare
If wife should dine at Edmonton,
    And I should dine at Ware."

So turning to his horse, he said
    "I am in haste to dine;
'Twas for your pleasure you came here,
    You shall go back for mine."

Ah! luckless speech, and bootless boast
    For which he paid full dear;
For while he spake, a braying ass
    Did sing most loud and clear;

90

Whereat his horse did snort, as he
    Had heard a lion roar,
And galloped off with all his might,
    As he had done before.

    Away went Gilpin, and away
        Went Gilpin's hat and wig;
    He lost them sooner than at first,
        For why?—they were too big.

Now Mistress Gilpin, when she saw
　　Her husband posting down
Into the country far away,
　　She pulled out half-a-crown;

And thus unto the youth she said
　　That drove them to the "Bell,'
"This shall be yours when you bring back
　　My husband safe and well."

The youth did ride, and soon did meet
　　John coming back amain;
Whom in a trice he tried to stop,
　　By catching at his rein.

But not performing what he meant,
    And gladly would have done,
The frighted steed he frighted more,
    And made him faster run.

Away went Gilpin, and away
    Went postboy at his heels,
The postboy's horse right glad to miss
    The lumbering of the wheels.

Six gentlemen upon the road,
    Thus seeing Gilpin fly,
With postboy scampering in the rear,
    They raised the hue and cry.

"Stop thief! Stop thief! A highwayman!"
    Not one of them was mute;
And all and each that passed that way
    Did join in the pursuit.

And now the turnpike-gates again
    Flew open in short space;
The toll-man thinking, as before,
    That Gilpin rode a race.

And so he did, and won it too,
    For he got first to town;
Nor stopped till where he had got up,
    He did again get down.

Now let us sing, Long live the King.
And Gilpin, long live he;
And when he next doth ride abroad,
May I be there to see.

The Steamboat and the Locomotive*

Gelett Burgess

ON the railway that ran through the City o' Ligg there was once a locomotive, who was always discontented and grumbling. Nothing in the world was good enough for him; or, at least, nothing in the City o' Ligg.

His coal was too hard or too soft; it was never just right. He hated to pull passenger trains because he had to go so fast, and he didn't like to pull freight trains because they were too heavy. He was always complaining that he was out of order, so that he might stay in the Round House and not work. He would shunt himself on sidings in hopes he might be forgotten; he was afraid to go over bridges, for fear they would break down; and he hated tunnels because they were so dark and cold. He thought iron rails were too soft to get good hold on, and he said that steel rails were altogether too slippery. He quarrelled with his tender, and he refused to be coupled up to one that he didn't fancy. He snorted and hissed at the semaphores and point signals, and he was a nuisance to the railway in more ways than can be told.

But, if he were bad, there was a young steamboat on the river who was worse. She was a very pretty craft, but that was no reason why she should insist on having a new set of paddle wheels *every* year. She was absurdly particular about her funnel, and, if it were not painted the exact color that she fancied she would declare that she

*Taken from *The Lively City o' Ligg*. Used by permission of the publishers, Frederick A. Stokes Company would scuttle herself. She would roll and pitch with anger if they tried to back her. She would dig up the middy bottom of the river with her paddles, and she gave a deal of trouble about steering.

When these ill-natured creatures came together at the dock in the river below the fortifications, they used to complain to each other till the cannon above them would cry, "Oh, I *say?*" and the bridge told them that they ought to be ashamed of themselves.

One day, after the steamboat had been carrying a load of noisy excursionists up from the harbor, she found the locomotive on the pier in a very gloomy state of mind.

"I'm not going to stand this any longer!" he said. "They've put me to hauling coal, and it's no work for a machine like me, especially when I can't burn any of it myself. I'm going to run away!"

"Well, that's a good idea; suppose I go with you, and we'll set out to seek our fortunes!" said the steamer.

They talked it all over, and finally decided to start that very night. The steamboat was to help the locomotive on the water, and the locomotive was to help the steamboat on the land. They were to share their wood and coal and water and have a jolly good time as long as they could.

At midnight the locomotive got on board the boat, and she steamed softly up the river. "This is fun!" said he.

"It's all right for you," said the boat, "but I must say you're heavier than I thought. Wait till it's *your* turn to give *me* a ride. I can't go much farther, anyway, the water is getting shallow. There's a dam up above here, so I think we'd better go ashore now."

She climbed up the bank with the locomotive's assistance, and he then hoisted her up on top of his cab, and set out across the fields. She was a little boat but she was heavy, and the locomotive puffed away with all his might through the grass, stopping to rest once in a while. So they went on for several days, turn and turn about, for they had to cross several lakes on the way.

After awhile, they began to approach a line of hills and the ground grew steeper and steeper, till at last the loco-motive could go no further with the steamboat on his back. So she got off and scrambled along for a few miles with her paddle wheels while the locomotive pushed her

BERT R. ELLIOTT

from behind. But the time came when neither of them could go a step further, and they lay on the ground exhausted. To make matters worse, they grew short of water and fuel. They cut down their rations to a ton of coal and a barrel of water a day, and even then they didn't have enough to take them back to either a forest or a lake.

It seemed likely that they would have to perish there on the hillside, and they quarrelled with each other peevishly, each accusing the other of being at fault for suggesting this terrible journey. The old river Wob and the railway of the City o' Ligg had never seemed so pleasant before, but, alas! it was many days' journey away.

Just as they began to think all hope was gone, one of them espied a dot in the sky. It grew larger and larger.

"It is a *balloon*?" they cried together, and they both began to blow their whistles with all the strength of the little steam that was left in their boilers.

The balloon came nearer and nearer, till it had got within hailing distance, and then they saw it was laughing almost hard enough to split its sides. It was a very fat, pink, round balloon, and, as it shook with merriment, its basket swung wildly above them.

"Well, I *declare*?" it cried out. "This is the queerest thing I ever saw! What in the world are you doing away up in these mountains? I never saw a locomotive or a steamboat on top of a hill before!"

"For heaven's sake, please don't laugh like that," cried the steamer, "but come and help us before we perish!"

The balloon finally consented to give them assistance over the mountains, and let down a rope, which the two tied around their waists. The balloon then rose, and the locomotive and steamboat were hoisted high in the air, and they all sailed away toward the East, across the range of mountains. They had floated for half a day in this way, when the balloon gave a pull up, a little harder than usual, and the rope suddenly broke! Down went the two, falling faster and faster and they thought their last moment had come. But, by good luck, they happened to fall in the middle of a large forest, and landed safely in an oak tree, without breaking a piece of machinery. Yet they had escaped one danger only to fall into another. They were lost in an immense wilderness and did not know where to turn.

The locomotive finally succeeded in climbing a tall tree, and made out smoke rising in the distance.

To this, they painfully made their way and, after a terrible struggle, came to an old saw-mill by the side of a little stream. It was a hideous old mill, of a villainous aspect that alarmed them both. But here was their only hope, and so the two unfortunate machines found them-

selves obliged to apply to the mill for shelter and fuel.

The mill welcomed them very hospitably, but there was something in his dusty, oily manner that the locomotive did not trust, and he resolved to stay awake and watch. The little delicate steamboat was, by this time, too exhausted to notice anything. After they had drunk many barrels of water each, they revived a little, and the mill offered them a few tons of sawdust, which, he said, was the only fuel he could give them. At the first trial the steamer whispered to the locomotive that it tasted queerly, but they decided it was only the oil in which it was soaked. At any rate they had to eat that or nothing, and they made a meal of it without more ado.

Hardly had they burned the last mouthful before they fell into a heavy sleep and knew nothing for many hours. The locomotive was awakened by a sudden pain, and he was terrified to find the teeth of a buzz-saw cutting through his side. He sprang up with a roar, but it was too late, his left side wheel had been bitten off! He charged furiously at the sides of the mill and tore open a great hole, then dragged out the steamboat, and ran her into the forest as fast as his five wheels could carry him.

As they stood trembling in the forest, a sudden glare of light attracted their attention. The mill was on fire, set, no doubt, from some sparks dropped by the locomotive in its terrible struggle for escape. By the light of the burning mill, they made their way through the forest. With new fuel and water, their strength had been partially renewed and terror increased their efforts.

In the morning, after a short sleep, they awoke to find themselves by the side of a wide river to which they had hobbled during the night, but had not seen in the dark. Alongside the bank of the stream ran a beautiful level railway line. They looked and looked, hardly able to believe their windows. It was too good to be true!

It did not take them long to decide what to do. The little steamboat gave one leap into the river and whistled long and merrily. The locomotive crawled onto the line, and rang its bell in a joyous peal. For they knew, by the looks of the country, that they had been travelling in a huge semi-circle and that the river and the railway led directly into the City o' Ligg.

So they steamed along, side by side, the lame locomotive and the sorrowful, shamefaced steamboat. That day one laid her head at last alongside the dock, and one puffed timidly into the station; both decided never to complain of any work that they should have to do in the future.

Little Gulliver*

LOUISA M. ALCOTT

UP IN the lighthouse lived Davy with Old Dan, the keeper. Most boys would have found it very lonely; but Davy had three friends, and was as happy as the day was long. One of Davy's friends was the great lamp, which was lighted at sunset and burned all night, to guide the ships into the harbor. To Dan it was only a lamp; but, to the boy, it seemed a living thing, and he loved and tended it faithfully. Every day he helped clean the big wick, polish the brass work, and wash the glass lantern which protected the flame. Every evening he went up to see it lighted and always fell asleep thinking, "No matter how dark the night, my good Shine will save the ships."

Davy's second friend was Nep, the Newfoundland, who was washed ashore from a wreck and who had never left the island since. Nep was rough and big, but no one could look in his soft, brown eyes and not trust him. He

*From *Aunt Jo's Scrap Bag*. Used by permission of the publishers, Little, Brown & Co.

followed Davy's steps all day, slept at his feet all night, and more than once had saved his life when Davy fell among the rocks, or got caught by the rising tide.

But the dearest friend of all was a sea gull. Davy found him with a broken wing, and nursed him till he was well. He was very fond of "Little Gulliver," as he called him. The bird came daily to talk with him, telling wild stories about his wanderings by land and sea.

Old Dan was Davy's uncle—a grim, gray man, who said little, did his work faithfully, and was both father and mother to Davy, who had no parents and no friends beyond the island. That was his world; and he led a quiet life among his playfellows, the wind and waves. He seldom went to the mainland, three miles away, for he was happier at home. He watched the sea anemones open below the water, found curious and pretty shells, and sometimes more valuable treasures washed up from some wreck. He saw little, yellow crabs and ugly lobsters. Sometimes a whale or a shark swam by, and often sleek, black seals came up to bask on the rocks. He gathered sea-weeds, from tiny red cobwebs to great scalloped leaves of kelp, longer than himself. He heard the waves dash and roar, the winds howl or sigh, and the gulls scream shrilly as they dipped and dived, or sailed away to follow the ships that came and went from all parts of the world.

With Nep and Gulliver, he roamed about his small kingdom; or, if storms raged, he sat up in the tower, safe and dry, watching the tumult of sea and sky. He never was afraid for Nep nestled at his feet, Dan sat close by, and overhead the great lamp shone far out into the night.

Close by the tower hung the fog bell, which would ring all night. One day Dan found that something among the chains was broken; and, having vainly tried to mend it, he decided to go to town and get what was needed.

"A heavy fog is blowing up and I must be off at once. I shall be back before dark," said Dan.

Away went the little boat; the fog shut down over it, as if a misty wall had parted Davy from his uncle. He sat and read for an hour, then fell asleep and forgot everything till Nep's cold nose on his hand waked him up. It was nearly dark; and, hoping to find Dan had come, he ran down to the landing-place. But no boat was there, and the fog was thicker than ever. Dan never had been gone so long before, and Davy was afraid something had happened to him. Then he cheered up and took courage.

"It is sunset by the clock; so I'll light the lamp, and, if Dan is lost in the fog, it will guide him home," said Davy.

Up he went, and soon the great star shown out above the black-topped lighthouse, glimmering through the fog, as if eager to be seen. Davy had his supper, but no Dan came. The fog thickened, the lamp was hardly seen, and no bell rang to warn the ships of the dangerous rocks. Poor Davy could not sleep, but all night long wandered from the tower to the door watching, calling, and wondering. At sunrise he put out the light, ate a little breakfast, and roved about the island hoping to see some sign of

Dan. The sun drew up the fog at last, and he could see the blue bay, the distant town, and a few fishing boats going out to sea. But nowhere was the island boat with gray Old Dan in it. Davy's heart grew heavier and heavier. In the afternoon Gulliver appeared. To him Davy told his trouble, and the three friends took counsel together.

"I've howled all day, hoping some one would hear me, but no one does and I'm discouraged," said Nep.

"I'll fly to town and try to learn what has become of Dan. Then I'll come and tell you. Cheer up, Davy. I'll bring you tidings!" With these cheerful words, away sailed Gulliver, leaving his master to watch and wait again.

The broken wing was not quite well, else Gulliver would have been able to steer clear of a boat that came swiftly by. A sudden gust drove the gull so violently against the sail that he dropped breathless into the boat, and a little girl caught him before he could recover himself. "Oh, what a lovely bird! I wanted a gull, and I'll keep this one."

Poor Gulliver struggled, pecked and screamed; but Dora held him fast, and shut him in a basket till they reached the shore. Then she put him in a lobster pot—a large wooden thing, something like a cage—and left him on the lawn where he could catch glimpses of the sea and watch the lighthouse tower, as he sat alone. For three long days and nights he was a prisoner, and suffered much. Boys poked and pulled him; little girls admired him. Cats prowled about his cage; dogs barked at him; hens cackled over him; and a shrill canary jeered at him from its pretty pagoda. Through the stillness of the night, he heard the waves break on the shore; the wind came singing up from the sea; the moon shone. But no one spoke a friendly word to him, and he pined away with a broken heart. On the fourth night, little Gulliver saw a black shadow steal across the lawn and heard a soft voice say:

"Poor bird, I'se gwine to let yer go. Specs little missy'll scold dreffle; jes wait till I gits de knots out of de string dat ties de door, and away you flies. You's a slave, like I was once; and it's a dreffle hard ting, I knows. I got away, and I means you shall."

"Do you live here? I never saw you playing with the other children," said the gull.

"Yes, I lives here, and helps de cook. You didn't see me, kase I never plays, de chil'en don't like me."

"Why not?" asked Gulliver, wondering.

"I'se black," said Moppet, with a sob.

"But that's silly," cried the bird. "The peeps are gray, the seals black, and the crabs yellow, but we are all friends."

"Nobody in de world keres for me." The black eyes grew so dim with tears that the poor child couldn't see that the last knot was out. Gulliver saw it, and, pushing up the door, flew from his prison with a glad cry.

"I wish you could go and live with Davy," whispered Gulliver. He told her all his story, and they agreed that he should fly to the island, and see if Dan was there. If not, he was to come back and Moppet would try to get someone to help find him. Full of hope and joy, Gulliver spread his wings; but alas, he was too weak to fly. For three days he had sat moping in the cage till his strength was gone.

"What shall I do?" he cried fluttering his feeble wings.

"I knows a little cove down yonder, where no one goes; and dere you kin stay till you's better. I'll come and feed you." As Moppet spoke, she took Gulliver in her arms and stole down to the lonely spot where nothing went but the winds and waves, the gulls, and little Moppet. Here she left the bird, and, with a loving "good-night," crept home to her bed in the garret, feeling rich as a queen.

Next day, a great storm came. The wind blew a hurricane, the rain poured, and the sea thundered on the coast. Gulliver spent an anxious day, sitting in a cranny of the rock, thinking of Davy and Moppet. At nightfall the storm raged fiercer than ever, and he gave up seeing Moppet for he was sure she wouldn't come through the pelting rain to feed him. But a voice cried through the darkness: "Is you dere, honey?" and Moppet came climbing over the rocks with a basket full of such bits as she could get.

"It's so stormy, I can't get to Davy; and I worry about him," began Gulliver. But, suddenly, a faint sound came up from below, as if someone called, "Help, help!"

"Hi! what's dat?" said Moppet, listening.

"Davy, Davy!" called the voice.

"It's Dan. Hurrah, we've found him!" Gulliver dived off the rocks so recklessly that he went splash into the water, but that didn't matter to him. Down by the seaside lay Dan, so bruised he couldn't move and so

faint with hunger he could hardly speak. As soon as
Gulliver called, Moppet scrambled down and fed the poor
man with her scraps, brought him rainwater from a nearby
crevice and bound his wounded head with her apron. Then
Dan told them how his boat had been run down by a ship
in the fog; how he was cast ashore in the lonely cove; how
he had lain there; how the sound of Moppet's voice told
him that help was near. How glad they all were! Moppet
danced for joy. Gulliver screamed and flapped his wings.

"What will Davy do? He may try to come ashore. Is
the lamp alight?" cried Dan.

Gulliver flew up to the highest rock, and looked out
across the dark sea. Yes, there it was, the steady star
shining through the storm and saying plainly, "All is well."

"Thank heaven! If the lamp is burning, Davy is alive!
Now, how shall I get to him?" said Dan.

"Never you fret, massa. Dere's folks in de house as'll
tend to you, ef I tells 'em where you is."

Off she ran and soon came back with help. Dan was taken to the house and carefully tended.

In the morning, Gulliver flew to the tower where Davy still watched and waited. He told his adventures, while Davy laughed and cried, and Nep wagged his tail for joy. Then came a boat to carry Davy ashore, while another keeper took charge of the light till Dan was well.

While Dan lay sick, Moppet tended him like a loving little daughter; and, when he was well, he took her for his own. It was a happy day when Dan and Davy, Moppet, Gulliver, and Nep sailed away to the island. The sun was setting, and they floated through waves as rosy as the rosy sky. A fresh wind filled the sail, and Gulliver sat on the masthead. Dan held the tiller and Davy lay at his feet, with Nep bolt upright beside him, but the happiest face of all was Moppet's. Kneeling at the bow, she leaned forward. Like a little black figurehead of Hope, she looked, as the boat flew on, bearing her away from the old life into the new.

As the sun sank, out shone the lamp with sudden brightness, as if the island bade them welcome. Dan furled the sail; and, drifting with the tide, they floated in, till the waves broke softly on the shore and left them safe at home.

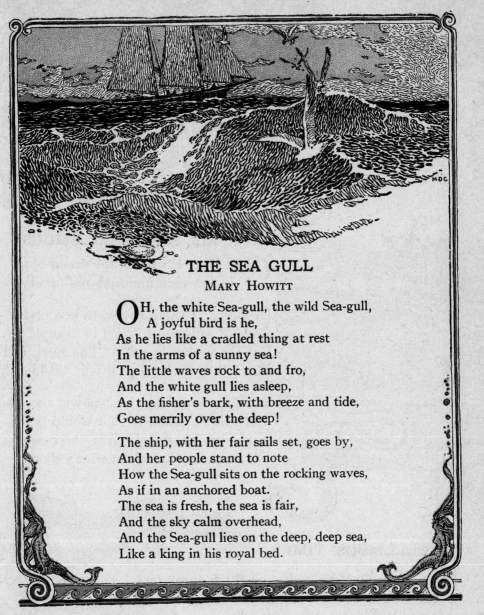

THE SEA GULL
MARY HOWITT

OH, the white Sea-gull, the wild Sea-gull,
  A joyful bird is he,
As he lies like a cradled thing at rest
In the arms of a sunny sea!
The little waves rock to and fro,
And the white gull lies asleep,
As the fisher's bark, with breeze and tide,
Goes merrily over the deep!

The ship, with her fair sails set, goes by,
And her people stand to note
How the Sea-gull sits on the rocking waves,
As if in an anchored boat.
The sea is fresh, the sea is fair,
And the sky calm overhead,
And the Sea-gull lies on the deep, deep sea,
Like a king in his royal bed.

ALL ABOUT COLUMBUS

COLUMBUS sailed the ocean blue
In fourteen-hundred-and-ninety-two.

He said: "I think the earth is round,
And I'll sail round it, I'll be bound!"
But the wise men said: "The earth is flat,
You'll fall off the edge if you sail like that,

You'll meet strange monsters in the sea,
And what a calamity that would be!"
But Columbus sailed and he sailed some more,
Till at last he found America's shore!

IN COLUMBUS' TIME*

SUPPOSE you lived then, do you think that you
Would believe what Columbus said was true
Or would you be like the wise men who
Laughed in his face and said, "Pooh, pooh?"
—Annette Wynne

*Taken from *For Days and Days*, by the kind permission of Frederick A. Stokes Company.

THE FIRST THANKSGIVING DAY

ALICE WILLIAMS BROTHERTON

IN PURITAN New England
  a year had passed away
Since first beside the Plymouth coast
    the English Mayflower lay,
When Bradford, the good Governor,
    sent fowlers forth to snare
The turkey and the wild fowl,
    to increase the scanty fare:—

"Our husbandry hath prospered,
    there is corn enough for food,
Though the peas be parched in blossom,
    and the grain indifferent good.
Who blessed the loaves and fishes
    for the feast miraculous,
And filled the widow's cruse,
    He hath remembered us!

"Give thanks unto the Lord of Hosts,
    by whom we all are fed,
Who granted us our daily prayer,
    'Give us our daily bread!'
By us and by our children
    let this day be kept for aye,
In memory of His bounty,
    as the land's Thanksgiving Day."

DOROTHY TODD

Each brought his share of Indian meal
    the pious feast to make,
With fat deer from the forest
    and wild fowl from the brake.
And chanted hymn and prayer were raised—
    though eyes with tears were dim.
"The Lord, He hath remembered us,
    let us remember Him!"

Then Bradford stood up at their head
    and lifted up his voice:
"The corn is gathered from the field,
    I call you to rejoice;
Thank God for all His mercies,
    from the greatest to the least,
Together we have *fasted*, friends,
    together let us *feast*.

"The Lord who led forth Israel
    was with us in the waste:
Sometime in light, sometime in cloud,
    before us He hath paced;
Now give Him thanks, and pray to Him
    who holds us in His hand—
To prosper us and make of this
    a strong and mighty land!"

From Plymouth to the Golden Gate
    to-day their children tread,
The mercies of that bounteous Hand
    upon the land are shed;
The "flocks are on a thousand hill,"
    the prairies wave with grain,
The cities spring like mushrooms now
    where once was desert-plain.

Heap high the board with plenteous cheer
    and gather to the feast,
And toast that sturdy Pilgrim band
    whose courage never ceased.
Give praise to that All Gracious One
    by whom their steps were led,
And thanks unto the harvest's Lord
    who sends our "daily bread."

WE THANK THEE

RALPH WALDO EMERSON

FOR flowers that bloom about our feet;
    For tender grass, so fresh, so sweet;
For song of bird, and hum of bee;
For all things fair we hear or see,
    Father in heaven, we thank Thee!
For blue of stream and blue of sky;
For pleasant shade of branches high;
For fragrant air and cooling breeze;
For beauty of the blooming trees,
    Father in heaven, we thank Thee!

115

George Washington and the First American Flag

IN A beautiful, big white house high above the Potomac River, George Washington, a kindly and dignified country gentleman, lived with Martha, his wife, and Martha's two jolly children, Jack and Patsey Custis. There were plenty of dogs and horses around the big estate. There were beautiful gardens also; and, from the fine green lawn, there was a splendid view over the Potomac River. Life was very happy in that pleasant, spacious home until sad times came for the country Washington loved so well.

This picture of Washington, riding around his estate at Mt. Vernon, and the one on page 117, are from Currier and Ives prints.

In those days, there was no United States at all. There were thirteen little colonies along the Atlantic Ocean where the people were chiefly farmers, living in plain little houses. These colonies had been settled by poor men and women from Europe, who had left the Old World behind because they found life so unhappy under the rule of bad kings.

In old-fashioned sailing vessels, they had crossed over endless miles of a stormy, wind-swept ocean. Arriving in the New World with little they could call their own, they found before them a wilderness, a land of unploughed soil and undisturbed, age-old forests through which the Indians slipped on their silent, moccasined feet. But they hewed the

From 1835-1895, these popular Currier and Ives prints, found in many American homes, recorded the history, customs, and life of the United States.

great trees in the forests, cleared the land, ploughed and planted it, fighting with the redskins when they chanced to be attacked. Thus, with unending toil, they turned the forbidding wilderness into prosperous farms, trying to make little homes for their swarming families of children. These people were chiefly English and the King of England was, therefore, king of these colonies, too. But the king of a country, which lay so many miles over the ocean, could know little of what was needed in a land he had never seen and in which he had little interest.

In fact, George III of England cared nothing about what was needed anywhere in his realm. What he wanted was money to spend and little did he care whether the means he took to get money out of his subjects were just or unjust, right or wrong. "Be a King, George!" the King's mother had said to him when he was only a boy; and George had grown up to believe that the only way to be a king was to make others do what he willed, whether they liked or no. Many people in England thought the King willful and headstrong; but, there, they could elect men to speak for them in parliament and keep the King under control.

In America it was different. The toiling American farmers, in their little, checkered, green fields so newly carved from the wilderness, were not allowed to send men to parliament to stand up for them to the King. The colonies were to George III nothing more than districts where he could get money easily without running any risk of having men talk back and balk him in his plans. Year after year, the wrongs he did the American colonists continued to grow greater until, at last, there was nothing that men of spirit could do, but stand up and fight for their rights.

It was a sad day for George Washington when he knew that this was true; for George still loved the old England from which his forefathers had come. He loved his family, too, and the beautiful country estate he was now obliged to leave. But he could not see great wrongs done and do nothing to set them right. Those strong men, who had faced all the dangers and difficulties of building homes in a wilderness, had dreamed that their labor was building a land where men should be free—not borne down and oppressed as they had been back in Europe. And now that great dream was in danger. The American dream of freedom for men and women to work with equal opportunity to better themselves in life was in danger of dying out before it had well begun. So George kissed his wife good-bye. His family and servants waved their last farewells from the lawn of lovely Mt. Vernon; and George, on his powerful horse, rode off to join the soldiers.

Years ago, when George was little more than a boy, he had fought against the Indians out on the western frontier; so he not only knew how to fight, but, more important still, he knew how to lead other men. Among all the leaders who gathered in Philadelphia to help the American people, Washington was the greatest. Hence he was appointed by the Congress of the Colonies, to be the commander-in-chief of the new American army.

Raw, awkward farmers they were, with little training in warfare, who left their ploughs, took their guns, and came to fight. The sleek, scarlet-coated soldiers in their splendid uniforms, who served King George III, laughed at these ungainly farmers; yet, under Washington's leadership, they soon became well-trained troops. They stood up with courage under fire against the soldiers of the King. Sometimes they lost a battle, and sometimes they won a great victory. But, whichever way their fortunes went, Washington kept them together, fighting for their freedom. His stepson, Jack Custis, was now old enough to be with him sometimes in campaigns, but the heart of the General never ceased to long for lovely Mt. Vernon.

On the Fourth of July, in 1776, the Continental Congress declared that the American colonies were henceforth independent of the mother country, England; and a very young,

This picture is from the painting, *The Declaration of Independence*, painted in 1816, by John Trumbull, a famous American painter of the time. It is in the Capitol, at Washington.

new nation was born to the family of nations—a youthful
United States, awkward and clumsy yet as an overgrown
country boy, but as full of promise, too, as lusty and as
strong. It had declared its firm faith in its Declaration
of Independence, that all men are created free and equal.

Then men and women began to say, in the crooked little
streets of Boston, on the water front in New York, among
the prim, red-brick houses of Quaker Philadelphia, and
through all the farms of the country: "We want a flag
of our own. We have hauled down the flag of old England
and we need a new banner to follow, a new sign of our
union to stand before the world."

Now Washington had heard of a woman named Betsy
Ross, who lived in Philadelphia. "The finest needlewoman
in America," Betsy Ross was called. There was just the
woman to make a new flag for the country. So, one fine
day in June, George Washington walked with two friends
through the pleasant streets of the quaint, old Quaker city.

In answer to his knock at the door of a trim red-brick house, Betsy Ross herself appeared, followed by her black cat, Powder; and, when she saw General Washington, she hastened to drop a curtsy.

"A fine day, Mistress Ross," Washington spoke in his usual pleasant and dignified manner. "We come to you on important business."

"You're very welcome, sir!" Betsy bobbed another curtsy; then she led the men into the house and into her little back parlor. "Now, sir, what can I do for you?" She was eager to know their errand.

The General answered her smiling: "Congress has just accepted a design for our new flag and so we've come to you, ma'am, to ask you to make it for us!"

Betsy beamed with pleasure. "I'll try my best," she said.

Then the General produced a paper on which was a drawing. "See," he said, "there are to be thirteen stripes, seven red ones and six white ones—one stripe for each of the colonies. And, in the upper left-hand corner, there will be a blue field with a circle of thirteen white stars—one star also for each of our colonies."

Betsy studied the drawing with interest.

"It's a beautiful design," she said, "but why have the stars six points? I see no reason for that."

The General heaved a gentle sigh. "The stars we have known so long on shields and coats-of-arms in England are always made with six points." He liked the star that reminded him of the land across the sea.

"If six-pointed stars are English, all the more reason why ours should be different!" Betsy cried with spirit. "Here, in our new world, we want to start life afresh. We must look at things through our own eyes, not through the eyes of our forefathers who lived long ago in England. Look up at the stars some night! You'll see they have only five points! If we're going to face life truly in this new country of ours, wouldn't it be better to place on our flag the stars just as we really see them, rather than as men have drawn them for so many ages past?"

General Washington's face was grave.

"I doubt very much," he said trying to find an excuse, "if you'll be able to cut a perfect five-pointed star."

Betsy seized a piece of paper, folded it, snipped with her scissors, opened the paper again and triumphantly held up to view a perfect five-pointed star!

The men with Washington smiled. "You're defeated, General!" they cried and even Powder, the cat, appeared to smile his approval.

An answering smile lit the face of General Washington. "So be it!" he agreed. "America's star shall be hers alone! God grant it may guide her to realize her dream!"

Thus it was that Betsy Ross made the first flag of the United States, the first Stars and Stripes! Hard were the battles Washington fought for several years after that, with the Stars and Stripes as his banner. Many were the dark days and the hardships he endured from the freezing Christmas night, when he crossed the Delaware River through the churning cakes of ice, to the terrible winter at Valley Forge, when his men were ragged and starving.

While Charles Peale and Gilbert Stuart were painting Washington in the European manner, American sign painters and home folks were painting him in their own purely American way. This 18th-century picture came from a Massachusetts tavern.

But, in time, the day of victory came when all the English King's troops had to leave American shores, and the little, new nation at last was free to thrive and grow. But then there remained for George Washington an even harder task. Not yet could he go back to live at his lovely Mt. Vernon, for he was elected first president of this young and sprawling republic. He it was who must keep the thirteen colonies together and lay the foundations for a government which he hoped, in time, would make real that great American dream of equal opportunities for all men and women to work and be justly rewarded for their work.

When Washington was finally free to go back home to Mt. Vernon, two more children, Eleanor Parke Custis and

This picture, which shows Lafayette being entertained at Mt. Vernon by the Washington family, is from a painting by T. P. Rossiter.

125

George Washington Parke Custis, the son and daughter of Jack Custis, brought life and laughter again into the big white house on the green lawns above the Potomac. There, as a country gentleman, Washington spent his last days.

From the time of George Washington on, the stripes on the American flag have remained thirteen in number, to remind men of those original thirteen plucky, little colonies who first fought so staunchly for freedom. But, as the hardy, adventurous American pioneers pushed west on foot or horseback or in great covered wagons as far as the Mississippi and west again to the Rockies and west to the far Pacific, swarming over the breadth of the continent, many new states were formed. And, as each new state joined the union, a new five-pointed star was added to the field of blue. Today, there are forty-eight stars representing the forty-eight states, which Americans won by toil in their battles with the wilderness. So, today, when the flag goes by, we remember all of this; but we think with deep feeling, too, of the more important fact that the Stars and Stripes were meant to stand in the hearts of Americans for the great American dream—the great American hope of a better world for all!

The Fourth of July

OLIVE BEAUPRÉ MILLER

H AIL Columbia, happy land!"
The band plays in the park,
And crowds of people everywhere
Are laughing in the dark.

Stars from Roman candles pop;
Pinwheels whirl in flame;
Huge big fiery letters write
George Washington's great name.

Siss, boom, bah! A golden snake,
Against the black of night,
Shoots up and up and up and bursts
To shower bouquets of light!

Hurrah for Independence Day!
Hurrah for the Fourth of July!
When rockets write the people's joy
In flames across the sky!

ABRAHAM LINCOLN*
1809-1865
ROSEMARY AND STEPHEN VINCENT BENÉT

LINCOLN was a long man.
He liked out of doors.
He liked the wind blowing
And the talk in country stores.

He liked telling stories,
He liked telling jokes.
"Abe's quite a character,"
Said quite a lot of folks.

Lots of folks in Springfield
Saw him every day,
Walking down the street
In his gaunt, long way.

Shawl around his shoulders,
Letters in his hat.
"That's Abe Lincoln,"
They thought no more than that.

HERBERT RUDEEN

*From *A Book of Americans*, published by Farrar & Rinehart, Inc. Copyright, 1933, by Rosemary and Stephen Vincent Benét.

OVER THE HILLS

A Story about Abe Lincoln

ONCE a tall, ungainly man—gaunt as a scraggly pine tree—walked the muddy streets of Springfield, Illinois. Everybody in town knew Abe Lincoln, of course. He had been born in a one-room log cabin somewhere down in Kentucky. Dennis Hanks, his cousin, used to tell how, as a boy, he ran hotfoot, to see the new baby when he heard that Abe was born. He found the mother and baby lying under a bearskin in a rude bed made of logs. So interested was young Dennis in this new arrival that he rolled up in a bearskin; slept all night on the floor; and insisted, in the morning, on holding the child in his arms. But the baby screwed up its face and cried without any letup. Dennis was disgusted.

"Take him, Aunt," said the boy, passing the child to a kinswoman. "He'll never grow up to be much!"

But in spite of this dire prophecy, when Abe was eight years old and the Lincoln family moved from Kentucky to Indiana, Abe was already able to help his father plough and to swing an axe like a man, cutting trees to build the new cabin. Between spells of work, Nancy Lincoln, his mother, scrubbed her little boy's face and sent him off to school.

"Abe, you go to school and larn all you kin," she said. So Abe and his sister trudged off, tramping through forests where bear, deer, and wildcats roamed for an eighteen-mile walk every day to and from the nearest log schoolhouse. How that boy loved to read! He wanted to learn, to live, to reach out for all the world of interesting things in books. He

read late every night, stretched on the floor by the fireplace. Dennis Hanks looked doubtful. Wildcats were then more plentiful than books in Indiana. "There's somethin' peculiarsome about Abe," Dennis said with a shake of his head.

Abe shot up like green corn, tall and lean and lanky. "Land o' Goshen!" said the neighbors. "How that boy air a-growin'!"

When he was nineteen, Abe was running a flatboat down the Mississippi carrying grain and produce to be traded at New Orleans, seeing negroes and white men in the cotton lands of the South, and meeting those wild boatmen who navigated the flatboats—half-horse and half-alligator, as they loved to call themselves.

When Lincoln lived in New Salem, Illinois, he kept a store by day and studied by night

On one of these trips, Abe's flatboat got stuck on a dam in the beautiful Sangamon River below the great, green ridge where stood the little log town of New Salem, Illinois. All the people of New Salem came out to watch the young boatman coolly save his cargo and get the boat off the dam.

So well did Abe like New Salem that he settled there for a time. In the bare, little cabins of the town, he soon had many friends. By the light of a fire made of shavings, he began to study law and soon he was elected to the Illinois State Legislature. His world kept growing bigger, till, by and by, there he was, moved to the city of Springfield, and now a rising young lawyer in the capital of the State.

The upper picture shows New Salem as it has been rebuilt and may be seen today.

Everybody in Springfield knew and liked Abe Lincoln. He was human through and through and his heart was as big and tender as that of any woman.

One day Abe and three friends, brother lawyers from Springfield, were riding on their horses down a muddy, country road. The sun was just coming out after a very hard rainstorm. Little raindrop diamonds glistened on the trees and the earth smelled rich and fresh. On either side, the young corn—new and tenderly green against the rich black of the earth—was running away from the road in straight diagonal lines, making the beautiful pattern which is the cornland's greeting to summer. As the men passed beneath an oak tree, they suddenly saw two robins fluttering overhead. Then they heard a faint chirping somewhere in the grass.

"What's the matter with those robins?" One of the men drew up his horse and looked at the birds for a moment.

"Probably the storm blew their little ones from the nest," the second lawyer said. "That's a pity, surely. They'll starve if they're not put back."

"What's the difference if they do starve?" The third man was very impatient. "Two less robins surely won't be missed in the world. Let's be on our way. If we don't hurry on to court, we'll be late for more important things."

The other two men who had spoken laughed at these remarks, chirruped to their horses gaily, and set off up the road. But Abe Lincoln stayed behind. Of course, it was nothing more than a little robin family who had fallen into difficulties; but Mr. and Mrs. Robin were very sad about it, and the little robins were surely in very great distress. Their chirping was growing fainter, though one of them now and then managed to give a sharp little screech.

Down from his horse sprang Abe. In the long grass he searched, while the parents anxiously eyed him. The robins were so tiny, it took him some minutes to find them. But when he came on the poor things, so awkward, forlorn, and ugly in their few little straggly feathers, he picked them up very gently and held them in his hand. Then he looked about to discover where their nest might be. In a moment more he spied it. It was high up in the tree. He would have to climb the tree to reach it. That wasn't so good for a man all dressed in his Sunday-best clothes, ready to appear in a law court and hoping to make an impression, not only on a dignified judge, but also on the members of the jury and the lawyers pitted against him. But still, what must be must be! You can't let little birds starve! So Abe climbed up the tree, altogether regardless of what might happen to his Sunday clothes.

He laid the two little birds gently in their nest; cozily they cuddled down, while their mother and father hovered in great satisfaction above. Then off went Abe at full gallop, hurrying on to court.

That was a little thing, but it was just like Abe Lincoln. When people or beasts were miserable, he could not rest till he helped them. Years later the United States was torn by the terrible questions that caused the Civil War. The North insisted that the South must free its negro slaves; the South insisted that each state had the right to settle such matters by and for itself. There was sorrow all over the Union.

Meantime, the name of Lincoln was becoming widely known throughout the United States. He had publicly debated with Senator Stephen A. Douglas the questions that troubled men. Crowds of people hailed him as Abe, the Giant Killer. "Link on to Lincoln!" they cried.

This picture is copied from an old print of Lincoln's debate with Douglas at Charleston, Illinois.

His name was in every man's mouth and so, in those unhappy days, it was Abraham Lincoln who was elected President. He left the rich cornlands of Illinois, amid which his tall, gaunt figure had been such a common sight. Off he went with his wife and young sons to live in the White House at Washington. It was a time that tried men's souls, and Lincoln's heart was torn; but he saw that the one great duty set him to perform was to keep together the Union which Washington had fought to found. Only as a people united, could the United States stand and hold its own among the nations! Only as a people united, could the United States fulfill the splendid dream it had had at its birth!

This picture of the Lincoln family in the White House, made by an artist of the time, shows President and Mrs. Lincoln with their sons, Robert, Thomas, and William.

War broke out soon after Lincoln entered the White House. Many were the brave men, like General Robert E. Lee, who fought for the South in the war; and many were the brave men who gave their lives for the North. When the North won the war, Lincoln deeply yearned to help the sorrowing South in its devastation and loss. He wanted to help build up its homes, replant its ravaged cotton fields, and restore all the hideous destruction that follows in the wake of war wherever men fight in the world. But, one night, he went to the theatre, and, as he was sitting in a box talking with Mrs. Lincoln, an assassin, running up behind him, suddenly fired a bullet which wounded him severely. The following morning, he died; and the man, who most deeply longed to help rebuild the South, was gone from the great position of President of the country.

It was many weary years, filled with many unhappy experiences, before the South could accomplish what Lincoln, had he lived, would so earnestly have helped them do. Nevertheless, with his guidance, Lincoln had saved the Union; and, in the years to come, North and South were to be more firmly knitted together than they had ever been in the old days before the war.

Wherever Lincoln went, whatever Lincoln did—whether it was as a boy living in a little log cabin, a struggling lawyer in Springfield, or President over a war-torn, unhappily struggling nation—he was always the same man who delayed his arrival in court and risked his Sunday-best clothes to put two ugly, little birds back up in their nest.

FOURSCORE AND SEVEN YEARS AGO OUR FATHERS BROUGHT FORTH ON THIS CONTINENT A NEW NATION, CONCEIVED IN LIBERTY AND DEDICATED TO THE PROPOSITION THAT ALL MEN ARE CREATED EQUAL. NOW WE ARE ENGAGED IN A GREAT CIVIL WAR, TESTING WHETHER THAT NATION, OR ANY NATION SO CONCEIVED AND SO DEDICATED, CAN LONG ENDURE. WE ARE MET ON A GREAT BATTLEFIELD OF THAT WAR. WE HAVE COME TO DEDICATE A PORTION OF THAT FIELD AS A FINAL RESTING PLACE FOR THOSE WHO HERE GAVE THEIR LIVES THAT THAT NATION MIGHT LIVE. IT IS ALTOGETHER FITTING AND PROPER THAT WE SHOULD DO THIS. BUT, IN A LARGER SENSE, WE CANNOT DEDICATE—WE CANNOT CONSECRATE—WE CANNOT HALLOW—THIS GROUND. THE BRAVE MEN, LIVING AND DEAD, WHO STRUGGLED HERE, HAVE CONSECRATED IT, FAR ABOVE OUR POOR POWER TO ADD OR DETRACT. THE WORLD WILL LITTLE NOTE NOR LONG REMEMBER WHAT WE SAY HERE, BUT IT CAN NEVER FORGET WHAT THEY DID HERE. IT IS FOR US THE LIVING, RATHER, TO BE DEDICATED HERE TO THE UNFINISHED WORK WHICH THEY WHO FOUGHT HERE HAVE THUS FAR SO NOBLY ADVANCED. IT IS RATHER FOR US TO BE HERE DEDICATED TO THE GREAT TASK REMAINING BEFORE US—THAT FROM THESE HONORED DEAD WE TAKE INCREASED DEVOTION TO THAT CAUSE FOR WHICH THEY GAVE THE LAST FULL MEASURE OF DEVOTION—THAT WE HERE HIGHLY RESOLVE THAT THESE DEAD SHALL NOT HAVE DIED IN VAIN—THAT THIS NATION, UNDER GOD, SHALL HAVE A NEW BIRTH OF FREEDOM—AND THAT GOVERNMENT OF THE PEOPLE, BY THE PEOPLE, FOR THE PEOPLE, SHALL NOT PERISH FROM THE EARTH.

In 1863, a crowd gathered at Gettysburg, to honor northern soldiers who had fallen there. Edward Everett gave a glowing address. It seemed that Lincoln could never equal him, but Lincoln's simple words live as a masterpiece, while Everett's are forgotten.

WHERE GO THE BOATS?*
Robert Louis Stevenson

Dark brown is the river,
  Golden is the sand.
It flows along forever,
  With trees on either hand.

Green leaves a-floating,
  Castles of the foam,
Boats of mine a-boating—
  When will all come home?

On goes the river,
  And out past the mill,
Away down the valley,
  Away down the hill.

Away down the river,
  A hundred miles or more,
Other little children
  Shall bring my boats ashore.

*Children of the 1890's and early 1900's waited eagerly for *St. Nicholas* with its drawings by Reginald Birch, a favorite illustrator, who created in pictures the character of Little Lord Fauntleroy, the hero of Frances Hodgson Burnett's famous story.

LITTLE SHEPHERD'S SONG
WILLIAM ALEXANDER PERCY

THE leaves, the little birds and I,
  The fleecy clouds and the sweet, sweet sky,
The pages shining as they ride
Down there, down there where the river is wide!
Heigh-ho what a day! What a lovely day!
Even too lovely to hop and play!

And so I lie in the deep, deep grass,
And watch the pages as they pass,
And sing to them as they to me,
Till they turn the bend by the poplar tree.
And then—O then, I sing right on,
To the leaves and the birds and myself alone!

              —13th Century

Why the Sea is Salt*

A Norse Folk Tale

GUDRUN THORNE-THOMSEN

ONCE on a time, but it was a long, long time ago, there were two brothers, one rich and one poor. Now, one Christmas eve, the poor one had not so much as a crumb in the house, either of meat or bread, so he went to his brother to ask him for something with which to keep Christmas. It was not the first time his brother had been forced to help him; and, as he was always stingy, he was not very glad to see him this time, but he said, "I'll give you a whole piece of bacon, two loaves of bread, and candles into the bargain, if you'll never bother me again, but mind you don't set foot in my house from this day on."

The poor brother said he wouldn't, thanked his brother for the help he had given him, and started on his way home. He hadn't gone far before he met an old, old man with a white beard, who looked so thin and worn and hungry that it was pitiful to see him. "In heaven's name give a poor man a morsel to eat," said the old man.

*From *East o' the Sun and West o' the Moon.* Used by special arrangement with the author and the publisher, Row, Peterson & Co.

"Now, indeed, I have been begging myself," said the poor brother, "but I'm not so poor that I can't give you something on the blessed Christmas eve." And with that he handed the old man a candle and a loaf of bread and he was just going to cut off a slice of bacon, when the old man stopped him. "That is enough and to spare," said he. "And now, I'll tell you something. Not far from here is the entrance to the home of the underground folks. They have a mill there which can grind out anything they wish for except bacon; now mind you go there. When you get inside they will all want to buy your bacon, but don't sell it unless you get in return the mill which stands behind the door. When you come out I'll teach you how to handle the mill."

So the man with the bacon thanked the other for his good advice and followed the directions which the old man had given him, and soon he stood outside the hillfolks' home. When he got in, everything went just as the old man had said. All the hillfolk, great and small, came swarming up to him like ants around an anthill and each tried to outbid the other for the bacon.

"Well!" said the man,, "by rights, my old dame and I ought to have this bacon for our Christmas dinner; but, since you have all set your hearts on it, I suppose I must give it up to you. Now, if I sell it at all, I'll have for it that mill behind the door yonder."

At first the hillfolk wouldn't hear of such a bargain and higgled and haggled with the man, but he stuck to what he said, and at last they gave up the mill for the bacon.

When the man got out of the cave and into the woods again, he met the same old beggar and asked him how to handle the mill. After he had learned how to use it, he thanked the old man and went off home as fast as he could; still the clock had struck twelve on Christmas eve before he reached his own door.

"Wherever in the world have you been?" asked his old dame. "Here have I sat hour after hour, waiting and watching, without so much as two sticks to lay under the Christmas porridge."

"Oh!" said the man, "I could not get back before, for I had to go a long way first for one thing and then for another; but now you shall see what you shall see."

So he put the mill on the table, and bade it first of all to grind out lights, then a tablecloth, then meat, then ale, and so on till they had everything that was nice for Christmas fare. He had only to speak the word and the mill ground out whatever he wanted. The old dame stood by blessing her stars, and kept on asking where he had got this wonderful mill, but he wouldn't tell her.

"It's all the same where I got it. You see the mill is a good one, and the mill stream never freezes. That's enough."

So he ground meat and drink and all good things to last out the whole of Christmas holidays; and on the third day, he asked all his friends and kin to his house and gave them a great feast. Now, when his rich brother saw all that was on the table and all that was in the cupboards, he grew quite wild with anger, for he could not bear that his brother should have anything.

" 'Twas only on Christmas eve," he said to the rest, "he was so poorly off that he came and begged for a morsel of food, and now he gives a feast as if he were a count or a king." Then he turned to his brother and said, "But where in the world did you get all this wealth?"

"From behind the door," answered the owner of the mill, for he did not care to tell his brother much about it. But later in the evening, when he had gotten a little too merry, he could keep his secret no longer and he brought out the mill and said:

"There you see what has gotten me all this wealth." And so he made the mill grind all kinds of things.

When his brother saw it, he set his heart on having the mill; and, after some talk, it was agreed that the rich brother was to get it at hay-harvest time, when he was to pay three-hundred dollars for it. Now, you may fancy the mill did not grow rusty for want of work; for while he had it, the poor brother made it grind meat and drink that would last for years. When hay-harvest came, the rich brother got it, but he was in such a hurry to make it grind that he forgot to learn how to handle it.

It was evening when the rich brother got the mill home; and next morning, he told his wife to go out into the hayfield and toss hay while the mowers cut the grass, and he would stay home and get the dinner ready. So, when dinner time drew near, he put the mill on the kitchen table and said, "Grind herrings and broth, and grind them good and fast." And the mill began to grind herrings and broth, first of all the dishes full, then all the tubs full, and so on till the kitchen floor was quite covered. The man twisted and twirled at the mill to get it to stop; but, for all his fiddling and fumbling, the mill went on grinding. In a little while the broth rose so high that the man was nearly drowned. So he threw open the kitchen door and ran into the parlor, but it was not long before the mill had ground the parlor full, too, and it was only at the risk of his life that the man could get hold of the latch of the housedoor through the stream of broth. When he got the door open, he ran out and set off down the road, with the stream of herrings and broth at his heels roaring like a waterfall over the whole farm.

Now, his old dame, who was in the field tossing hay, thought it a long time to dinner, and at last she said:

OVER THE HILLS

"Well! though the master doesn't call us home, we may as well go. Maybe he finds it hard work to boil the broth, and will be glad of my help."

The men were willing enough, so they sauntered homewards. But, just as they had got a little way up the hill, what should they meet but herrings and broth all running and dashing and splashing together in a stream and the master, himself, running before them for his life. As he passed them he called out: "Eat, drink! Eat, drink! but take care you're not drowned in the broth."

Away he ran as fast as his legs would carry him to his brother's house and begged him in heaven's name to take back the mill, at once, for, said he, "If it grinds only one hour more the whole parish will be swallowed up by herrings and broth."

So the poor brother took back the mill, and it wasn't long before it stopped grinding herrings and broth.

And now he set up a farmhouse far finer than the one in which his brother lived; and with the mill, he ground so much gold that he covered it with plates of gold.

As the farm lay by the seaside, the golden house gleamed and glistened far away over the sea. All who sailed by put ashore to see the rich man in the golden house, and to see the wonderful mill the fame of which spread far and wide, till there was nobody who hadn't heard of it.

So one day there came a skipper who wanted to see the mill, and the first thing he asked was if it could grind salt.

"Grind salt!" said the owner. "I should just think it could. It can grind anything."

When the skipper heard that, he said he must have the mill; for, if he only had it, he thought he need not take his long voyages across stormy seas for a lading of salt. He much preferred sitting at home with a pipe and a glass. Well, the man let him have it, but the skipper was in such a hurry to get away with it that he had no time to ask how to handle the mill. He got on board his ship as fast as he could and set sail. When he had sailed a good way off, he brought the mill on deck and said, "Grind salt, and grind both good and fast"

And the mill began to grind salt so that it poured out like water; and, when the skipper had got the ship full, he wished to stop the mill. But, whichever way he turned it and however much he tried, it did no good. The mill kept on grinding, the heap of salt grew higher and higher, and at last down sank the ship.

There lies the mill at the bottom of the sea and grinds away to this very day, and that is the reason why the sea is salt—so some folks say.

Heidi in the Alpine Pasture

JOHANNA SPYRI*

HEIDI was awakened by a loud whistle; and, as she opened her eyes, a yellow sunbeam fell on her bed and turned it, and all the hay that was spread about the loft, to glistening gold. She looked about her with astonishment, and could not make out where she was. Soon she heard her grandfather's deep voice, and it all came back to her—how she came there, and that, now, she lived with her grandfather up on the Alm. Springing up, she soon had on all her clothes. Down the ladder she ran, and away out-of-doors. There stood Peter, the goatherd, with his goats; and her grandfather brought out his from the stall, that they might join the flock. "Would you like to go with Peter to the pasture?" asked the old man.

The child jumped for joy. Her grandfather then went into the hut, and soon called out to Peter:

"Come here, goat-general, and bring your knapsack."

Peter obeyed in surprise and opened his bag, in which was his poor, little dinner.

"Wider! Wider!" said the old man, and put in a big piece of bread and another piece of cheese. "Now the mug goes in, too, for the little one can't drink as you do from the goats themselves. And you must milk this twice full at noon, for the child will go with you, and stay till you come back in the evening. Now, take care that she does not fall off the cliffs."

*Johanna Spyri, born in 1827, in a pretty village near Zurich, is one of Switzerland's favorite writers. She used to visit friends high up in the mountains and wrote charming stories of simple Swiss mountain life.

Heidi was soon ready, and off they went, climbing joyfully up the Alm. The green Alp was covered with blue and yellow flowers, and their wide-open petals seemed laughing back at the sun, while everything shimmered and shone. Hiedi scampered hither and thither, shouting for joy. Gathering great handfuls of flowers, she stuffed them all into her apron; for she must carry them home with her.

Poor Peter was obliged to keep his eyes about him today, for the goats were like Heidi; they ran about everywhere, while Peter must whistle and shout and swing his rod to bring together all the wanderers.

"Where have you gone, Heidi?" he called out.

"Here," came back the reply from somewhere. Peter could see no one, for Heidi sat on the ground behind a little mound that was covered with flowers; and the whole air was perfumed.

"Come here now!" shouted Peter. "We have still a good bit to climb; so come along! Up there, at the very top, sits the old eagle and screams!"

This stirred the little girl. She jumped up and ran toward her companion, with her apron full of flowers.

She now kept along with Peter; and the goats, too, went in better order, for they scented the sweet herbs from their pasture on the heights afar.

As they now had reached the highest point, Peter took off his knapsack, placing it carefully in a little hollow where it would be sheltered from the wind. He did not mean to see his knapsack, with the nice dinner, go rolling down the hillside. Then he stretched himself his full length on the sunny sod, to rest after the steep climb.

Heidi seated herself beside Peter, and looked about her on every side. Below lay the valley in the full glow of the morning sun; before her was a huge, white snow field rising toward the dark-blue heaven; to the left, an enormous mass of rocks was piled  up, on each side of which stood a pillar of rock, bald and jagged against the blue sky. All was still. Only a light, soft breeze stirred the blue harebells and the shining, yellow buttercups, that grew all about, and stood nodding on their slender stalks. Peter had fallen asleep, while the goats climbed here and there and up into the bushes. Never was the child so happy in her life.

Thus a long time passed, and Heidi gazed at the needles of rock above her so long that they seemed to have gotten faces and to be returning her gaze like old friends—when, suddenly, she heard above her a loud, sharp scream. As she looked up, a huge bird circled overhead. With widespread wings, it soared through the air; and, in great sweeps, came back again and again—screaming loud and piercingly over Heidi's head.

"Peter! Peter! Wake up!" cried Heidi aloud. "See, the eagle is here! Look! Look!"

Peter roused himself at her cry; and the children gazed at the bird, which rose higher and higher, disappearing at last in the blue ether over the gray rocks.

"Where is he now?" asked Heidi, who had watched the bird with breathless interest.

"In his home up there."

"Oh, how beautiful to live up there. Let us climb up there to see his home," suggested Heidi.

"Oh, oh, oh!" cried Peter. "Even the goats are not able to climb up there, and the Alm uncle said you must not fall over the cliff."

After this Peter began to whistle and the goats came running and jumping, and were soon all gathered on the green field. Some nibbled at the sweet grass; others ran here and there; while some stood opposite each other, a little way apart, and butted playfully with their horns.

Springing to her feet, Heidi ran in amidst the goats, and jumped from one to another to make herself acquainted with each separately, for each had its own peculiarities, and looked and behaved differently.

While Heidi played with the goats, Peter had fetched the knapsack and arranged the food in a square on the grass. Then he filled the mug with fresh milk from Schwanli, and placed it in the middle of the square.

Then he called to Heidi to come, and the table looked so inviting, that she hopped about it for joy.

"Stop dancing about, it is time to eat!" said Peter.

"Is the milk for me?" asked Heidi, as she took her seat.

"Yes," he replied, "and, when you have emptied the mug, you can have another full from Schwanli."

"And where do you get your milk?" asked the little girl curiously.

"From my goat, from Snail. Do begin!"

Heidi began at last with the milk; and when she had emptied the mug, Peter rose and filled it again. Heidi broke some of her bread into it, and then handed the rest of it to Peter. It was a big piece, twice as large as his which he had already eaten. She also gave him her big lump of cheese, saying, "You can have it all, I have had enough." Peter stared with his big eyes in speechless astonishment, for never in his life had he been able to say that he had had enough and could give something away.

When he saw that she was serious, he took his present, nodded his thanks, and made the heartiest meal that had fallen his share since he first tended the goats. While he ate, Heidi watched the flock.

"What are their names, Peter?" said she.

So he began and named them one after the other without hesitating, and pointed at each with his finger. Soon Heidi, too, could name them all.

There was the big Turk with his strong horns, who was forever butting the others. Only the bold and slender Thistlebird did not avoid him—and the little, white Snowball, who was always bleating beseechingly. Often Heidi ran to it, taking its head between her hands to comfort it. The animal nestled confidingly against the little girl, and was quiet again; and Peter called out from his seat, explaining Snowball's trouble between each mouthful.

"She does that because her old one does not come with us any more. She was sold to Mayenfeld the day before yesterday, and will not come any more to the Alm."

"Who is the old one?" asked Heidi.

"Pooh! its mother," was the reply.

"Where is the grandmother?" asked the child.

"Has none."

"Or the grandfather?"

"Has none."

"Oh, you poor little Snowball!" said Heidi tenderly, pressing the goat softly to her side. "But now don't cry so anymore; I will come here every day with you, then you will not be lonely."

Snowball rubbed her head trustingly on Heidi's shoulder and bleated no more.

When Peter had finished his dinner, he came again to look after his flock. By far the loveliest and cleanest of the goats were Schwanli and Barli. The animals had begun again to climb up toward the bushes, each in its own way; some springing lightly over every obstacle, others carefully searching all along the way for a good mouthful, Turk trying now and then to give someone a blow, Schwanli and Barli climbing prettily and lightly. Heidi stood with her hands behind her back, watching all that went on.

Suddenly Peter sprang to his feet, and was after the goats with great leaps; away he went through the flock toward the side of the Alp, where the rocks rose up steep and naked. He saw that the giddy Thistlebird had strayed in that direction and had reached the very edge of the precipice. As he was about to seize her, he tripped and fell, catching her only by the leg as he came down; but he held her fast, though she bleated with surprise and anger to find herself held, while she persisted in pressing forward. Peter called loudly for Heidi. He was unable to rise, and seemed to himself almost pulling the little goat's leg off, she was so determined to go on. In a trice Heidi was there. Pulling quickly a sweet-smelling herb, she held it under Thistlebird's nose, saying soothingly, "Come, little goat! Come and be good, Thistlebird." The goat turned quickly about to nibble at the herb, and was quite content.

But Peter, having regained his feet, hastened to seize the string that hung from her collar, while Heidi took the collar from the other side; and they led the wanderer between them to rejoin the rest of the flock, which was peaceably feeding below.

Almost unheeded the day had passed, and now the sun was beginning to sink behind the mountain. Heidi sat quietly on the ground, gazing at the harebells and blue-bells, as they shone in the golden light, watching how the grass took a golden hue, and how the rocks above began to shimmer and flash. Suddenly she started to her feet, shouting, "Peter! Peter! It is burning! It is on fire! All the mountains flame, and the great snow yonder, and the sky! Look! Look! The highest peak is glowing! Oh, the beautiful fire! Now look, Peter, it has reached the eagle's nest! See the rock! See the pines! Everything burns!"

"It is always like that, but it is no fire," said Peter.

"What is it, then?" cried Heidi, and ran about in every direction to look; for she could not see enough of it stand-ing still, it was so beautiful everywhere.

"It comes of itself," explained the lad.

"Look! Look now!" she screamed, in the wildest excite-ment. "Just this minute it is all as red as roses. Look at the snow and those high, pointed rocks!"

"Oh, the lovely, rosy snow! And all over the rocks are roses! Oh, now they are growing gray! It is going!

It has all gone, Peter!" and little Heidi threw herself on the ground, looking as unhappy as if it were the end to all the beauty in the world.

"It will be just so again to-morrow," said the lad. "Get up, we must go home now." So he whistled the herd together, and they set out.

Heidi scarcely spoke a word until the Alm hut came in sight, and she saw her grandfather sitting on his bench outside, waiting for the goats. Then she ran to him quickly, with Schwanli and Barli at her heels.

Peter called out, "Come again, to-morrow! Good-night." And the child gave him her hand, promising to go to-morrow and bidding good-bye to the departing goats. She put her arm about the neck of little Snowball especially saying, "Good-night, Snowball. Sleep well! Don't forget that I am going with you again to-morrow, and you must not bleat so sadly again."

Then Heidi came back under the pine tree, calling out before she could reach her grandfather: "Oh, it was so beautiful! The fire, and the roses on the rock!"

"Yes," said her grandfather, "the sun does that when he says good-night to the mountains. He casts his most beautiful beams across them, so that they will not forget he is coming again in the morning." This pleased the little girl, and she could scarcely wait until the morrow. But first she must go to sleep; and she did sleep in her little hay bed, and dreamed of pink mountains covered with roses in the midst of which Snowball jumped gayly about.

Boots and His Brothers

SIR GEORGE WEBB DASENT*

ONCE on a time there was a man who had three sons, Peter, Paul, and John. John was Boots, of course, because he was the youngest. I can't say the man had anything more than these three sons, for he hadn't one penny to rub against another; and so he told his sons they must go out into the world and try to earn their bread. Now, a bit off the man's cottage was the king's palace, and just against the king's windows a great oak had sprung up, so big that it took away all the light. The king had said he would give many dollars to the man who could fell the oak, but no one was man enough for that; for, as soon as one chip of the oak's trunk flew off, two grew in its stead. A well, too, the king would have dug. All his neighbors had wells, but he hadn't any, and that he thought a shame. So the king said he would give anyone who could dig him such a well as would hold water for a whole year round, both money and goods; but no one could do it, for the king's palace lay high, high up on a hill, and they hadn't dug a few inches before they came upon the living rock.

*Dasent is one of the famous collectors of Norse folk tales. He did for the Norse people what the Grimms did for the Germans and Joseph Jacobs for the English. From *Popular Tales from the Norse*, published by G. P. Putnam's Sons.

But as the king had set his heart on having these two things done, he had it given out far and wide that he, who could fell the big oak in the king's courtyard and get him a well that would hold water the whole year round, should have the Princess and half the kingdom. Well, you may easily know there was many a man who came to try his luck, but, for all their hacking and hewing and all their digging and delving, it was no good. The oak got bigger and stouter at every stroke, and the rock didn't get softer either. So, one day, those three brothers thought they'd set off and try and their father hadn't a word against it, so Peter, Paul, and Jack went off from their home.

Well, they hadn't gone far before they came to a fir wood and up along one side of it rose a steep hillside; and, as they went, they heard something hewing and hacking away up on the hill among the trees.

"I wonder now what it is that is hewing away up yonder," said Jack.

"You're always so clever with your wonderings," said Peter and Paul. "What wonder is it, pray, that a woodcutter should stand and hack up there on a hillside?" "Still, I'd like to see what it is," said Jack. And up he went. "Oh, if you're such a child, 'twill do you good to go and take a lesson," bawled out his brothers.

But Jack didn't care for what they said; he climbed the steep hillside toward where the noise came; and, when he reached the place, what do you think he saw? Why, an axe that stood there hacking and hewing, all of itself, at the trunk of a fir. "Good-day!" said Jack. "So you stand here all alone and hew, do you?"

"Yes. Here I've stood and hewed and hacked a long, long time, waiting for you," said the Axe.

"Well, here I am at last," said Jack, as he took the axe, pulled it off its haft, and stuffed both head and haft into his wallet.

So when he got down again to his brothers, they began to jeer at him. "And now, what funny thing was it you saw up yonder on the hillside?" they said.

"Oh, it was only an axe we heard," said Jack.

So, when they had gone a bit farther, they came under a steep rock and up there they heard something digging and shoveling. "I wonder now," said Jack, "what it is digging and shoveling up yonder at the top of the rock."

"Ah, you're always so clever with your wonderings," said Peter and Paul again, "as if you'd never heard a woodpecker hacking and pecking at a hollow tree."

"Well," said Jack, "I think it would be a piece of fun just to see what it really is." So off he set to climb the rock; and, when he got near the top, what do you think he saw? Why, a spade that stood there digging and delving.

"Good-day!" said Jack. "So you stand here all alone, and dig and delve!"

"Yes," said the Spade, "and that's what I've done this many a long day, waiting for you."

"Well, here I am," said Jack again, as he took the spade and knocked it off its handle, put it into his wallet, and then went down again to his brothers.

"Well, what was it, so rare and strange," said Peter and Paul, "that you saw up there at the top of the rock?"

"Oh," said Jack, "nothing more than a spade."

So they went on again a good bit, till they came to a brook. "I wonder now," said Jack, "where all this water comes from."

"Where the brook comes from, indeed!" said Peter and Paul in one breath. "If you're not mad already, you'll go mad very soon with your wonderings. Have you never heard how water rises from a spring in the earth?"

"Yes; but, still, I've a great fancy to see where this brook comes from," said Jack. So up he went; and, as he went, the brook got smaller and smaller. At last, a little way farther on, what do you think he saw? Why, a great walnut, and out of that the water trickled.

"Good-day!" said Jack again. "So you lie here, and trickle and run down all alone?"

"Yes, I do," said the Walnut, 'and here have I trickled and run this many a long day, waiting for you."

"Well, here I am," said Jack, as he took up a lump of moss and plugged up the hole, that the water mightn't run out. Then he put the walnut into his wallet, and ran down to his brothers.

"Well, now," said Peter and Paul, "have you found out where the water comes from?"

"Oh, it was only a hole it ran out of," said Jack; and so the others laughed and made game of him again.

So when they had gone a bit farther, they came to the king's palace. But as everyone in the kingdom had heard how they might win the Princess and half the realm if they could only fell the big oak and dig the king's well, so many had come to try their luck that the oak was twice as big as it had been, for two chips grew for every one they hewed out with their axes. So the king had now laid down, as a punishment, that anyone who tried and failed should be put on a barren island and both his ears should be clipped off. But the two brothers didn't let themselves be scared by that, they were quite sure they could fell the oak; and Peter, as he was the eldest, was to try his hand first; but it went with him as with all the rest who had hewn at the oak; for every chip he cut out, two

grew in its place. So the king's men seized him and clipped off both his ears and put him out on the barren island.

Now Paul was to try his luck, but he fared just the same; so the king's men seized him too, clipped his ears, and put him off on the island. So now Jack was to try.

"We're quite ready to clip your ears at once, and then you'll save yourself some bother," said the King, for he was angry with him for his brother's sake.

"Well, I'd like just to try first," said Jack and he took his axe out of his wallet and fitted it to its haft. "Hew  away!" said he to his axe; and away it hewed, making the chips fly again, so that it wasn't long before down came the oak. When that was done, Jack pulled out his spade, and fitted it to its handle. "Dig away!" said he to the spade; and so the spade began to dig and delve till the earth and rock flew out in splinters, and so he had the well soon dug out, you may think.

And, when he had got it as big and deep as he chose, Jack took out his walnut and laid it in one corner of the well and pulled the plug of moss out.

"Trickle and run!" said Jack; and so the nut trickled and ran, till the water gushed out of the hole in a stream and in a short time the well was brimful.

Since Jack had felled the oak which shaded the King's palace and dug a well in the palace yard, he got the Princess and half the kingdom, as the King had promised. Everyone said, "Well, after all, Jack wasn't so much out of his mind when he took to wondering."

The Nuremberg Stove*
LOUISE DE LA RAMÉE

AUGUST lived in a little town called Hall in Austria. His mother was dead, his father was poor, and there were many mouths at home to feed. This night was terribly cold, but he kept up his courage by saying: "I shall soon be at home with dear Hirschvogel." The snow outlined with white every gable and cornice of the beautiful, old, wooden houses; the moonlight shone on the gilded signs that hung before the doors. Here and there a ruddy firelight lit up a homely interior, with the noisy band of children clustering around the housemother.

At August's knock, the oak door of his father's house flew open. It was a large, barren room into which he rushed; but, at the top of the chamber, sending out warmth and color, was a tower of porcelain, surmounted with armed figures and shields and a great golden crown on the summit of all. It was a stove of 1532, the handwork of the great potter, Augustin Hirschvogel.

*Nuremberg was once an art center for Germany. Longfellow calls it "quaint old town of art and song," and Wagner's opera, *Die Meistersinger von Nürnberg*, portrays its famous mastersingers of the 16th Century.

The stove, no doubt, had stood in palaces and been made for princes; had warmed the crimson stockings of cardinals and the gold-broidered shoes of archduchesses. It was a right royal thing. Yet, perhaps, it had never been more useful than it was now in this poor, desolate room, sending down heat and comfort to the troop of children tumbled together on a wolfskin at its feet.

"Oh, dear Hirschvogel, I am so cold!" said August, kissing its gilded lion's claws. "Is father not in, Dorothea?"

"No, dear. He is late."

Dorothea was seventeen, the eldest of the Strehla family; there were ten of them in all. Next to her, came Jan and Karl and Otho, big lads, gaining a little for their own living. And then came August, who went up in the summer to the high Alps with the farmers' cattle, but in winter could do nothing. And then all the little ones, who could only open their mouths to be fed like young birds—Albrecht and Hilda, and Waldo and Christof, and last of all little three-year-old Ermengilda, with eyes like forget-me-nots.

The father was a good man, but weak and weary with so many to find food for and so little to do it with. He worked at the salt furnaces; and, by that, gained a few florins. Very poor they were, and Dorothea's heart ached with shame, for she knew that their father's debts were many for flour and meat and clothing. Of fuel to feed the big stove, they had always enough without cost, for their mother's father was alive and sold wood and fir cones and coke, and never grudged them to his grandchildren.

"Father says we are never to wait for him. We will have supper, now you have come home, dear," said Dorothea.

Supper was a huge bowl of soup, with big slices of brown bread swimming in it, and some onions bobbing up and down. The bowl was soon emptied by ten wooden spoons; and then the three eldest boys slipped off to bed, being tired with their rough bodily labor in the snow all day. Dorothea drew her spinning wheel by the stove and set it whirring, and the little ones got August down upon the old worn wolfskin and clamored to him for a picture or a story. For August was the artist of the family.

He had a piece of planed deal, that his father had given him, and some sticks of charcoal and he would draw a hundred things he had seen in the day—faces and dogs' heads, and men in sledges. It was all very rough, for there was no one to teach him anything, but it kept the whole troop of children shrieking with laughter or watching breathlessly with wide-open, wondering eyes.

They were all so happy; what did they care for the snow outside? Their little bodies were warm, and their hearts merry; and August cried, as he looked at the stove shedding its heat on them all: "Oh, dear Hirschvogel, you are almost as great and good as the sun! No, you are greater and better, because he goes away all these dark, cold hours; but you—just a bit of wood to feed you—and you make a summer for us all the winter through!"

The grand old stove seemed to smile through all its iridescent surface at the praises of the child. The grandfather Strehla, who had been a master mason, had dug it up out of some ruins where he was building, and only thought it worth finding because it was such a good one to burn. Ever since then the stove had stood in the big, empty room—having seen nothing prettier in all its many years than the children tumbled now in a cluster, like gathered flowers, at its feet.

To the children, the stove was a household god. In summer, they dressed it up with green boughs and the numberless beautiful wild flowers of the Tyrol. In winter, all their joys centered in it; and, scampering home from school over the ice and snow, they were happy knowing that they would soon be cracking nuts or roasting chest-

nuts in the broad, ardent glow of its noble tower with all
its spires and pinnacles. All the children loved the stove;
but, with August, the love of it was a passion, and in his
secret heart he used to say to himself, "When I am a man,
I will make just such things!" For August was a dreamer
of dreams, and when high up on the Alps with the stillness
and the sky around him, he was quite certain that he would
live for greater things than driving the herds up when the
springtide came among the blue sea of gentians.

In the midst of the chatter and laughter, a blast of
frozen air struck like ice through the room. It was the
father who had come home. The younger children ran to
meet him, but Karl Strehla responded wearily to the

young ones' welcome. "Take the children to bed," he said, and Dorothea obeyed. August stayed behind, curled before the stove. When Dorothea came down again, suddenly Karl Strehla struck his hand on the table.

"I have sold Hirschvogel," he said; and his voice was husky in his throat. "I have sold Hirschvogel to a traveling trader for two-hundred florins. What would you? I owe double that. He will take it to Munich tomorrow."

Dorothea gave a low cry, "Oh, Father!—the children—in midwinter!" She turned white as the snow without.

August stood staring with dazed eyes. He gave a shriek and threw himself down at his father's feet.

"Oh, Father!" he cried, his hands closing on Strehla's knees. "You cannot mean what you say! Send *it* away—our life, our sun, our joy, our comfort? You could not do such a thing! It is a living thing, and it loves us and we love it with all our hearts! Oh, listen! I will go and try and get work tomorrow! I will ask them to let me cut ice or make the paths through the snow. Oh, Father, do hear me, for pity's sake!"

Strehla was moved by the boy's anguish. Every word of the child stung him with a sense of shame. He despised himself for the barter of the heirloom of his race. "You are a little fool," he said, harshly, as they had never heard him speak. "Get up and go to bed. The stove is sold and goes to Munich tomorrow."

Then Strehla took the oil-lamp and stumbled off to bed.

August threw himself on the stove, covering it with kisses, and sobbing as though his heart would burst.

"Come to bed, dear. Oh, don't lie and look like that!" sighed his sister.

"I shall stay here. They might take it in the night!"

"But it is cold! The fire is out."

"It will never be warm any more, nor shall we."

All his childhood had gone out of him, all his gleeful, careless, sunny temper. To him it was as if the end of the world had come. His sister lingered by him while striving to persuade him to go to his place in the little crowded bedchamber with Albrecht and Waldo and Christof. But it was in vain. "I shall stay here," was all he answered her. And he stayed—all the night long. The lamps went out; the rats came and ran across the floor; the cold intensified and the air of the room grew like ice. Whilst yet it was dark, his three elder brothers let themselves out—each going to his work. His sister came down with a light in her hand. August shuddered all over. "It is the morning!" he said.

Loud blows with the heavy, iron knocker drowned his words. A strange voice called aloud: "Let me in! Quick! I am come to take the great stove."

August sprang erect, his fists doubled, his eyes blazing.

"You shall never touch it!" he screamed.

"Who shall prevent us?" laughed a big man, amused at the fierce little figure fronting him.

"I!" said August. "You shall never have it!"

"Strehla," said the big man, as August's father entered the room, "you have got a little mad dog here, muzzle him."

August fought like a little demon, and hit out right and left. But he was soon mastered by four grown men, and his father flung him with no light hand out the door.

When Dorothea stole out to look for August, he was nowhere in sight. She went back to little Gilda and sobbed, whilst the others stood looking on, dimly understanding that with Hirschvogel was going all the warmth of their bodies and the light of their hearth.

August stood still for a time leaning against the back wall of the house. Then his heart fluttered with a new idea. Why not go with the stove? He ran out of the court-

yard and across to the huge Gothic porch of the church.
From there he could watch unseen his father's door.

Presently his heart gave a great leap, for he saw the
straw-enwrapped stove brought out and laid with infinite
care on the bullock dray. The sleigh-wagon slowly crept
over the snow of the place. Then he crept, unseen by any
of his brothers or sisters, out of the porch and followed
in the wake of the dray. A desperate resolve made itself
up in August's mind. Where Hirschvogel went, he would
go. How he managed it he never knew; but certain it is
that, when the goods-train moved out of Hall, August
was hidden behind the stove in the great, covered truck.

It was very dark in the truck, but August was not frightened, he was close to Hirschvogel and presently he meant to be closer; for he meant to do nothing less than get inside Hirschvogel itself. Having by great luck two silver groschen in his pocket, which he had earned the day before by chopping wood, he had bought some bread and sausage at the station. This he ate in the darkness.

When he had eaten, he set to work like a little mouse to make a hole in the straw and hay which enveloped the stove. He gnawed and nibbled and pulled, making his hole where he guessed that the opening of the stove was, the opening through which he had so often thrust the big, oak logs to feed it. At last he found the door of the stove, which he knew was quite large enough for a child of his age to slip through. Slip through he did, as he had often done at home for fun, and curled himself up there to see if he could remain during many hours.

He found that he could, air came  in through the brass fretwork of the stove. He leaned out, drew the hay and straw together, and re-arranged the ropes so that no one could ever have dreamed a little mouse had been at them. Then he curled himself up again and went fast asleep. The train lumbered on and, when he awoke, it was quite dark. For awhile he was sorely frightened and sobbed in a heartbroken fashion, thinking of them all at home.

It took all the short winter's day and the long winter's night and half of another day to go over ground that the mailtrains cover in a forenoon. The train passed pretty Rosenheim, and here the Nuremberg stove was lifted out heedfully and set under a covered way. The boy was tossed to and fro as the men lifted the huge thing, and the walls of his beloved fire king were not cushions of down.

He had still some of his loaf and a little of his sausage. What he did begin to suffer was thirst. But, fortunately for him, the stove, having been marked "fragile and valuable," was not treated like a mere bale of goods; and the Rosenheim stationmaster resolved to send it on by a passenger train that would leave there at daybreak.

Munich was reached; and August, shaking like a little aspen leaf, felt himself once more carried out on the shoulders of men, rolled along on a truck, and finally set down, where he knew not, only he knew he was thirsty—so thirsty! He thought he had been moved on this truck many miles; but, in truth, the stove had been only taken from the railway station to a shop in the Marienplatz. On its gilded feet it now stood in the small, dark curiosity-shop of one Hans Rhilfer.

"I shall not unpack it till Anton comes," he heard a man's voice say; and then he heard a key grate in a lock. He concluded he was alone, and ventured to peep through the straw and hay. What he saw was a small, square room filled with pictures, carvings, old steel armor, shields, daggers, Chinese idols, and all the rubbish of a *bric-a-brac* dealer's. It seemed a wonderful place; but, oh! was there one drop of water in it all? There was not a drop of water, but beyond the window was a wide stone ledge covered with snow. August darted out of his hiding-place, ran and opened the window, crammed the snow into his mouth, and then flew back into the stove.

Presently the key turned in the lock, he heard heavy footsteps and the voice of the man who had said to his father, "You have a little mad dog, muzzle him!" The voice said, "You have called me a fool many times. Now you shall see what I have got for two-hundred dirty florins!"

Then the two men approached more closely, and the heart of the child went pit-a-pat. They began to strip the stove of its wrappings.

"A right royal thing!" Sublime! Magnificent!" they said.

August fancied at times they quarreled, for they swore lustily. He made out that they were going to show Hirschvogel to some great person.

Presently the door opened again sharply. He could hear the two dealers' voices murmuring unctuous words. The voice of another person, more clear and refined than theirs, answered them curtly. The child could distinguish little that he said, except the name of the king and the word "gulden" again and again. After awhile, he went away. Then the dealers also withdrew, double-locking the door.

After a time, August dropped asleep. Midnight was

chiming when he awoke and, all being still, ventured to put his head out the door of the stove to see why such a strange, bright light was round him. What he saw was nothing less than all the *bric-a-brac* in motion.

A tall, Dutch clock was going through a gavotte with a spindle-legged chair; an old violin of Cremona was playing itself; a Japanese bronze was riding along on a griffin. Little Dresden cups and saucers were skipping and waltzing; the teapots with their broad, round faces were spinning their own lids like teetotums; and a little Saxe poodle with a red ribbon at its throat, was running from one to another. A lovely, little lady all in pink and gold and white, with powdered hair and high-heeled shoes all made of the finest Meissen china, tripped up to August and smiled and led him out to a minuet. "I am the Princess of Saxe-Royale," she said with a smile.

Then he ventured to say to her, "Madame, my Princess, could you tell me kindly why some of the figures dance and speak and some lie up in a corner like lumber?"

"My dear child," said the powdered lady, "those silent, dull things are *imitation*, lies, falsehoods, fabrications! They only *pretend* to be what we *are?*"

Then from where the great stove stood, there came a solemn voice. All eyes turned upon Hirschvogel, and the heart of its little human comrade gave a great jump of joy.

"My friends," said that clear voice, "we were made in days when men were true creators, and so we, the work of their hands, are true, too. Our makers wrought at us with zeal, with integrity, with faith—not to win fortunes, but to do nobly an honest thing and create for the honor of the Arts and God. I see amidst you a little human

thing who loves me. Now I want him forever to remember that we are what we are, because those who were of single mind so created us, scorning sham and haste and counterfeit. Where I go now I know not; but, since I go from that humble house where they loved me, I shall be sad and alone."

Then the voice sank away in silence, and a strange golden light that had shone on the great stove faded away. The clocks of the city struck six of the morning. August awoke with a start and found himself lying on the bare bricks of the floor, and all the *bric-a-brac* was lying quite still all around.

He rose slowly to his feet. Tramp, tramp, came a heavy step up the stair. He had but a moment in which to scramble back into the great stove, when the door opened and the two dealers entered, bringing candles with them to see their way. The dealers undid the shutters and then began to wrap up the stove once more in all its straw and hay. Presently they called up their porters, and the stove, heedfully swathed and tended as though it were some prince going on a journey, was borne on the shoulders of six stout Bavarians down the stairs and out the door. Even behind all those wrappings August felt the icy bite of the intense cold at dawn of a winter's day in Munich.

The stout carriers tramped right across Munich to the railway station. Whether for a long or a short journey, whether for weal or woe, the stove with August still within it, was once more hoisted up into a great van; but this time it was not all alone, and the two dealers as well as the six porters were all with it.

OVER THE HILLS

Though the men grumbled about the state of the roads and the season, they were hilarious and well-content, for they laughed often; and August, like the shrewd little boy he was, thought to himself, with a terrible pang, "They have sold Hirschvogel for some great sum! They have sold him already!"

It is but an hour and a quarter that the train usually takes to pass from Munich to the Lake of Starnberg; but this morning the journey was much slower, because the way was encumbered by snow. When it did reach Possenhofen, the stove was lifted out once more. August could see through the fretwork of the brass door a calm and noble piece of water with low, wooded banks and distant mountains. Before he had time to get more than a glimpse of the green, gliding surface, the stove was again lifted up and placed on a large boat that was in waiting. The boat then moved across the lake to Leoni.

"Now, men, for a stout mile and a half!" said one of the dealers to his porters. Encouraged by large promises, they shouldered sullenly the Nuremberg stove, grumbling again at its preposterous weight, but little dreaming that they carried within it a small, panting, trembling boy. The road seemed terribly long to the poor little man inside the stove as he kept sinking and rising, sinking and rising with each of their steps.

After a very long time August lost the sense of the fresh, icy wind blowing on his face through the brasswork above. Then he heard a great many voices, and, as he felt a warm

air come to him, he concluded that he was in some heated chambers. There was a delicious fragrance in the air—a fragrance as of flowers. "Only how can it be flowers?" thought August. "It is November!" From afar off, as it seemed, there came dreamy, exquisite music. He did not know it, but he was in the royal castle of Berg, and the music he heard was the music of Wagner, who was playing in a distant room.

Presently he heard a low voice say, close behind him, "So! It was well-bought! It is exceedingly beautiful! It is undoubtedly the work of Augustin Hirschvogel."

Then the hand of the speaker turned the round handle of the door, and the fainting soul of the poor little prisoner grew sick with fear. The door was slowly drawn open, someone bent down and looked in, and the same voice called aloud in surprise, "What is this in it? A live child!"

Then August, dominated by one master passion, sprang out of the stove and fell at the feet of the speaker.

"Oh, let me stay! Pray, *mein Herr*, let me stay!" he sobbed. "I have come all the way with Hirschvogel!"

Some gentlemen's hands seized him, not gently by any means, and their lips muttered in his ear, "Little knave, peace! Be quiet! Hold your tongue! It is the King!"

But the voice he had heard said in kind accents, "Poor child! He is very young. Let him go. Let him speak to me."

F M McAnelly

Richard Wagner (1813-1883), the great German composer, whose music August heard, is the man in the black cap at the right of the picture. King Ludwig II, of Bavaria, friend of all artists, invited Wagner to Munich.

The angry and astonished chamberlains let August slide out of their grasp. The young man said to him, "My child, how come you here, hidden in this stove?"

"Oh, dear King!" said August, "Hirschvogel was ours. We have loved it all our lives, and father sold it. I pray you to let me live with it. I will go out every morning and cut wood for it, if only you will let me stay beside it."

There was that in the child's face which pleased and touched the king. "What is your name?" he asked.

"August Strehla." The boy's lips quivered with a sob.

"Have you traveled in this stove all the way from Tyrol?"

"Yes," said August, "no one thought to look inside till you did." The king laughed; then another view of the matter occurred to him. "Who bought the stove of your father?" he inquired.

"Traders of Munich," said August.

"What sum did they pay, do you know?"

"Two-hundred florins," said August.

The king turned to his gentlemen-in-waiting and desired that the dealers be brought before him. Then he had water and wine brought, and cake also for August, who, though he drank eagerly, could not swallow anything.

"May I stay with Hirschvogel?" he said.

"Wait a little," said the king, and asked abruptly, "what do you wish to be when you are a man?"

"A painter. I wish to be what Hirschvogel was. I mean the master that made *my* Hirschvogel."

"I understand," said the king.

Then the two dealers were brought to their sovereign.

"Did you buy this stove of this boy's father for two-hundred florins?" the king asked, and his voice was no longer soft and kind, but very stern.

"Yes, your Majesty," murmured the trembling traders.

"And how much did the gentleman, who purchased it for me, give to you?"

"Two-thousand ducats!" muttered the dealers.

"You will give at once to this boy's father the two-thousand gold ducats that you received, less the two-hundred Austrian florins that you paid him," said the king. "You are great rogues. Be thankful you are not more greatly punished."

August heard and felt dazzled, yet miserable. Two-thousand ducats for his father! Why, his father would never need to go any more to the salt-baking! And yet, whether for ducats or for florins, Hirschvogel was sold just the same, and would the king let him stay with it?

"Oh, do! please do!" he murmured.

"Will I let you stay with your Hirschvogel?" said the king. "Yes, I will. You shall stay at my court and you shall be taught to be a painter. And if, when you are twenty-one-years old, you have done well and bravely, then I will give you your Nuremberg stove."

Then he smiled and stretched out his hand. The courtiers tried to make August understand that he ought to bow and touch it with his lips, but August was too happy. He threw his arms about the king's knees.

HIAWATHA'S CHILDHOOD*
HENRY WADSWORTH LONGFELLOW

BY THE shores of Gitche Gúmee,
By the shining Big-Sea-Water,
Stood the wigwam of Nokómis.
Dark behind it rose the forest,
Rose the black and gloomy pine-trees,
Rose the firs with cones upon them;
Bright before it beat the water,
Beat the clear and sunny water,
Beat the shining Big-Sea-Water.

    There the wrinkled, old Nokómis
Nursed the little Hiawátha,
Rocked him in his linden cradle,
Bedded soft in moss and rushes,
Stilled his fretful wail by saying,
"Hush! the Naked Bear will hear thee!"
Lulled him into slumber, singing.

*The cantata, *Hiawatha's Childhood*, by Bessie Whiteley presents, in the rhythm of Indian music, this lovely tale of the child, Hiawatha. Reprinted by permission of the publishers, Houghton Mifflin Company.

At the door on summer evenings
Sat the little Hiawátha,
Heard the whispering of the pine-trees,
Heard the lapping of the water,
    Saw the fire-fly, Wah-wah-tay'-see,
Flitting through the dusk of evening,
With the twinkle of its candle
Lighting up the brakes and bushes,
And he sang the song of children,
Sang the song Nokómis taught him:
"Wah-wah-tay'-see, little fire-fly,
Little, flitting, white-fire insect,
Little, dancing, white-fire creature,
Light me with your little candle,
Ere upon my bed I lay me,
Ere in sleep I close my eyelids!"
Saw the moon rise from the water,
Rippling, rounding from the water,

Saw the rainbow in the heaven,
In the eastern sky, the rainbow,
Whispered, "What is that, Nokómis?"
And the good Nokómis answered:
" 'Tis the heaven of flowers you see there;
All the wild-flowers of the forest,
All the lilies of the prairie,
When on earth they fade and perish,
Blossom in that heaven above us."

When he heard the owls at midnight,
Hooting, laughing in the forest,
"What is that," he said, "Nokómis?"
And the good Nokómis answered:
"That is but the owl and owlet,
Talking in their native language,
Talking, scolding at each other."

Then the little Hiawátha
Learned of every bird its language,
Learned their names and all their secrets,
How they built their nests in Summer,
Where they hid themselves in Winter,
Talked with them whene'er he met them,
Called them "Hiawátha's Chickens."

Of all beasts he learned the language,
Learned their names and all their secrets,
How the beavers built their lodges,
Where the squirrels hid their acorns,
How the reindeer ran so swiftly,
Why the rabbit was so timid,
Talked with them whene'er he met them,
Called them "Hiawátha's Brothers."

Little Diamond and the North Wind*

GEORGE MACDONALD

I HAVE been asked to tell you about the back of the North Wind. I am going to tell you how it fared with a boy who went there. He lived in a low room over a coach house. Indeed, I am not sure whether I ought to call it a room; for it was just a loft where they kept hay and straw and oats for the horses. And when little Diamond—but stop, I must tell you that his father who was a coachman, had named him after a favorite horse—when little Diamond, then, lay there in bed, he could hear the horses under him munching away in the dark, or moving sleepily in their dreams. For Diamond's father had built him a bed in the loft with boards all round it, because they had so little room in their own end over the coach house.

*George MacDonald (1824-1905) the friend of Lewis Carroll and John Ruskin, broke away from the sternness of a past generation, giving children beautiful fairy stories. From *At the Back of the North Wind*.

There was hay at his feet and hay at his head, piled up in great trusses to the very roof. Indeed it was sometimes only through a little lane with several turnings, which looked as if it had been sawed out for him, that he could reach his bed at all. Sometimes, when his mother had undressed him in her room and told him to trot away to bed, he would creep into the heart of the hay, and lie there thinking how cold it was outside in the wind, and how warm it was inside there in his bed, and how he could go to it when he pleased, only he wouldn't just yet; he would get a little colder first. And ever as he grew colder, his bed would grow warmer, till at last he would scramble out of the hay, shoot like an arrow into his bed, cover himself up, and snuggle down, thinking what a happy boy he was. He had not the least idea that the wind got in at a chink in the wall, and blew about him all night. For the back of his bed was only boards an inch think, and on the other side of them was the north wind.

Now, as I have already said, these boards were soft and crumbly. Hence little Diamond found one night after he lay down, that a knot had come out of one of them, and that the wind was blowing in upon him in a cold and rather imperious fashion. Now he had no fancy for leaving things wrong that might be set right; so he jumped out of bed again, got a little strike of hay, twisted it up, folded it in the middle, and, having thus made it into a cork, stuck it into the hole in the wall. But the wind began to blow loud and angrily; and, as Diamond was falling asleep, out blew his cork and hit him on the nose, just hard enough to wake him up quite. He searched for his hay-cork, found it, stuck it in harder, and was just dropping off once more, when, pop! with an angry whistle, the cork struck him again, this time on the cheek. Up he rose once more, made a fresh stopple of hay, and corked the hole severely. But he was hardly down again before— pop! it came on his forehead. He gave it up, drew the clothes above his head, and was soon fast asleep.

Although the next day was very stormy, Diamond forgot all about the hole. His mother, however, discovered it, and pasted a bit of brown paper over it, so when Diamond snuggled down the next night, he had no occasion to think of it.

Presently, however, he lifted his head and listened. Who could that be talking to him? The wind was rising again, and getting very loud, and full of rushes and whistles. He was sure someone was talking—

and very near him, too. But he was not frightened, so he sat up and hearkened. At last the voice, which, though quite gentle, sounded a little angry, appeared to come from the back of the bed. He felt about with his hand, and came upon the piece of paper his mother had pasted over the hole. Against this he laid his ear, and then he heard the voice quite distinctly. "What do you mean, little boy—closing up my window?"

"What window?" asked Diamond.

"You stuffed hay into it three times last night. I had to blow it out again three times."

"You can't mean this little hole! It isn't a window. It's a hole in my bed."

"I did not say it was *a* window. I said it was *my* window."

"But it can't be a window, because windows are holes to see out of."

"Well, that's just what I made this window for."

"But you are outside; you can't want a window."

"You are quite mistaken. Windows are to see out of, you say. Well, I'm in my house, and I want windows to see out of it."

"But you've made a window into my bed."

"Well, your mother has got three windows into my dancing room and you have three into my garret. Just open this window."

"Mother says I shouldn't be disobliging; but it's rather hard. You see the north wind will blow right in my face if I do."

"I am the North Wind"

"O-o-oh!" said Diamond, thoughtfully. "Then will you promise not to blow on my face if I open your window?"

"You shall not be the worse for it—I promise you that." Feeling with his little sharp nails, Diamond got hold of the open edge of the paper and tore it off. In came a long, whistling spear of cold, and struck his little naked chest. He scrambled in under the bedclothes, and he felt a little—not frightened exactly—but rather queer; for what a strange person this North Wind must be that lived in the great house called Out-of-Doors, and made windows into people's beds! But the voice began again, and he could hear it quite plainly.

"What is your name, little boy?" it asked.

"Diamond," answered Diamond, under the bedclothes.

"What a funny name!"

"Diamond is a very pretty name, Mr. North Wind," persisted the boy, vexed that it should not give satisfaction. "Diamond is a great and good horse; and he *sleeps* right under me. He's Big Diamond, and I'm Little Diamond; and I don't know which of us my father likes best."

A laugh, large but musical, sounded somewhere beside him, but Diamond kept his head under the clothes.

"I'm not Mr. North Wind," said the voice.

"You told me you were the North Wind," insisted Diamond.

"I did not say *Mister* North Wind," said the voice.

"Well, then, I do, for mother tells me I ought to be polite."

"You can't say it's polite to lie there talking with your head under the bedclothes, and never look up to see what kind of person you are talking to. I want you to come out with me."

"I want to go to sleep," said Diamond, very nearly crying.

"You shall sleep all the better to-morrow night. Will you take your head out of the bedclothes?" said the voice.

"No!" answered Diamond, half-peevish, half-frightened. The instant he said the word, a tremendous blast of wind crashed in a board of the wall and swept the clothes off Diamond. He started up in terror. Leaning over him was the large, beautiful, pale face of a woman.

Her dark eyes looked a little angry, for they had just begun to flash; but a quivering in her sweet upper lip made her look as if she were going to cry. What was most strange was that away from her head streamed out her black hair in every direction, so that the darkness in the hayloft looked as if it were made of her hair; but as Diamond gazed at her in speechless amazement, mingled with confidence—for the boy was entranced with her mighty beauty—her hair began to gather itself out of the darkness, and fell down all about her again, till her face looked out of the midst of it like a moon out of a cloud. From her eyes came all the light by which Diamond saw her face and her hair, and that was all he did see of her yet. The wind was over and gone.

"Will you go with me now, little Diamond? I am sorry I was forced to be so rough," said the lady.

"I will! Yes, I will!" answered Diamond, holding out both his arms. "Please, North Wind, you are so beautiful, I am quite ready to go with you."

"You must not be ready to go with everything beautiful all at once, Diamond. What if I should look ugly without being bad—look ugly myself because I am making ugly things beautiful? What then?"

"I don't quite understand you, North Wind."

"Well, I will tell you. If you see me with my face all black, don't be frightened. If you see me flapping wings like a bat's, as big as the whole sky, don't be frightened. If you hear me raging ten times worse than Mrs. Bill, the blacksmith's wife—even if you see me looking in at people's windows like Mrs. Eve Dropper, the gardener's wife—you must believe that I am doing my work. Nay, Diamond, if I change into a serpent or a tiger, you must not let go your hold of me. If you keep a hold, you will know who I am all the time. Do you understand?"

"Quite well" said little Diamond.

"Come along, then," said North Wind.

Diamond crept out of bed and followed her. North Wind laughed merrily, and went tripping on faster. Her grassy robe swept and swirled about her steps; and, wherever it passed over withered leaves, they went fleeing and whirling in spirals and running on their edges like wheels, all about her feet. They were now climbing the slope of a grassy ascent. The moment they reached the top, North Wind stood and turned her face toward London. The stars were still shining clear and cold overhead. The air was sharp, but Diamond did not find it cold.

"Now," said the lady, "whatever you do, do not let my hand go. I am getting ready to sweep one of my rooms. Those careless, greedy, untidy children leave it in such a mess." As she spoke he could have told by her voice, if he had not seen with his eyes, that she was growing larger and larger. Her head went up and up toward the stars; and, as she grew, her hair also grew—longer and longer, and lifted itself from her head, and went out in black waves. The next moment, however, it fell back around her, and she grew less and less till she was only a tall woman. Then she gathered some of her hair, and began weaving and knotting it together. When she had done, she bent down her beautiful face close to his, and said: "Diamond, I am afraid you would not keep hold of me, so I have been making a place for you in my hair. Come!"

194

Diamond held out his arms; she took him in her hands, threw him over her shoulder, and said, "Get in, Diamond."

And Diamond parted her hair with his hands, crept between, and, feeling about, soon found the woven nest. It was just like a pocket, or like the shawl in which gipsy women carry their children. North Wind felt all about the nest; and, finding it safe, said, "Are you comfortable, Diamond?"

"Yes, indeed!" answered Diamond.

The next moment he was rising in the air. North Wind grew towering up to the place of the clouds. Her hair went streaming out from her, till it spread like a mist over the stars. She flung herself abroad in space.

Diamond held on by two of the twisted ropes which formed his shelter. He peeped through the woven meshes, for he did not dare to look over the top of the nest. The earth was rushing past like a river or a sea below him. Trees and water and green grass hurried away beneath. Chimney pots fell, and tiles flew from the roofs. There was a great roaring, for the wind was dashing against London like a sea; but, at North Wind's back, Diamond felt nothing of it. He was in a perfect calm. He could hear the sound of it, that was all.

By and by he raised himself and looked over the edge of his nest. There were the houses rushing up and shooting away below him, like a fierce torrent of rocks instead of water. Then he looked up to the sky, but could see no stars; they were hidden by the blinding masses of the lady's hair which swept between. He began to wonder whether she would hear him if he spoke. He would **try**.

"Please, North Wind," he said, "what is that noise?"

From high over his head came the voice of North Wind:

"The noise of my besom. I am the old woman that sweeps the cobwebs from the sky, only I'm busy with the floor now."

"What makes the houses look as if they were running away?"

"I'm sweeping so fast over them."

"But, please, North Wind, I knew London was very big, but it seems as if we should never get away from it."

"We are going round and round, else we should have left it long ago."

"Please, would you mind going a little slower, for I want to see the streets?"

"You won't see much now."

"Why?"

"Because I have swept nearly all the people home."

But she dropped a little toward the roofs of the houses, and Diamond could see down into the streets. There were very few people about, though. The lamps flickered and flared again. Suddenly Diamond espied a little girl coming along a street. She was dreadfully blown by the wind, and a broom she was trailing behind her was very troublesome. It seemed as if the wind had a spite at her—it kept worrying her like a wild beast, and tearing at her rags. She was so lonely there!

"Please, North Wind," he cried, "help that little girl!"

"No, Diamond; I mustn't leave my work."

"But why shouldn't you be kind to her?"

"I am kind to her; I'm sweeping the smells away."

"But you're kinder to me, dear North Wind. Why shouldn't you be as kind to her as you are to me?"

"There are reasons, Diamond. Everybody can't be done to all the same. Everybody is not ready for the same thing. Of course, you can help her if you like. You've got nothing particular to do at this moment. I have!"

"Oh, do let me help her, then! But you won't be able to wait, perhaps?"

"No, I can't wait; you must do it yourself."

"I want to go," said Diamond. "Only there's just one thing—how am I to get home?"

"Well, though I cannot promise to take you home," said North Wind, as she sank nearer and nearer to the tops of the houses, "I can promise you will get home somehow. Have you made up your mind what to do?"

The same moment North Wind dropped into the street and stood, only a tall lady, but with her hair flying up over the housetops. She took Diamond and set him down in the street. The same moment he was caught in the fierce coils of the blast, and all but blown away. North Wind stepped back a pace, and at once towered in stature to the height of the houses. A chimney pot crashed at Diamond's feet. He turned in terror, but it was to look for the little girl, and when he turned again the lady had vanished, and the wind was roaring along the street. The little girl was scudding before the blast, her hair flying too, and behind her, she dragged her broom. Diamond crept into the shelter of a doorway, thinking to stop her, but she passed him like a bird, crying pitifully.

"Stop, little girl!" shouted Diamond, starting in pursuit.

"I can't" wailed the girl. "The wind won't let go of me."

Diamond could run faster than she, and he had no broom. In a few moments he had caught her by the frock. But it tore in his hands, and away went the little girl. So he had to run again, and this time he ran so fast that he got before her and turning round caught her in his arms, when down they went both together, which made the little girl laugh in the midst of her crying.

"Where are you going?" asked Diamond.

"Home," she said, gasping for breath.

Then I will go with you," said Diamond.

And then they were silent for awhile, for the wind blew worse than ever, and they had both to hold on to a lamppost.

"Where is your crossing?" asked the girl at length.

"I don't sweep," answered Diamond.

"What *do* you do, then?" asked she.

"I don't know what I do do," answered he, feeling rather ashamed. "My father's Mr. Coleman's coachman."

"Have you a father?" she said, staring at him as if a boy with a father was a natural curiosity.

"Yes. Haven't *you?*" returned Diamond.

199

"No; nor mother neither. Old Sal's all I've got."
She began to cry again. "If she was my mother, she
wouldn't lie abed and laugh to hear me crying at the door."

"You don't mean she won't let you in to-night?"

"It'll be a good chance if she does."

"We'd better have a try anyhow. Come along," said
Diamond, taking her hand, "and I'll take care of you."

She led him, turning after turning, until they stopped
at a cellardoor in a very dirty lane. There she knocked.

"I shouldn't like to live here," said Diamond.

"Oh, yes, you would, if you had nowheres else to
go," answered the girl. "I only wish we may get in."

"I don't want to go in," said Diamond.

"Where do you mean to go, then?"

"Home to my home."

"Where's that?"

"I don't exactly know."

"Then you're worse off than I am."

"Oh no, for North Wind—"
began Diamond,
and stopped.

M.S.H.

"*What?*" said the girl, as she held her ear to the door, listening.

But Diamond did not reply. Neither did old Sal.

"I told you so," said the girl. "She is wide awake hearkening. But we don't get in."

"What will you do, then?" asked Diamond.

"Move on," she answered.

"Where?"

"Oh, anywheres. Bless you, I'm used to it. Come on!"

"Hadn't you better come home with me, then?"

"That's a good joke, when you don't know where home is. Come on."

"But where?"

"Oh, nowhere in particular. Come on."

Diamond obeyed. The wind had now fallen considerably. They wandered on and on, turning in this direction and that, without any reason for one way more than another, until they had got out of the thick of the houses into a waste kind of place. By this time they were both very tired. Diamond felt a good deal inclined to cry, and thought he had been very silly to get down from the back of the North Wind, not that he would have minded it if he had done the girl any good, but he thought he had been of no use to her. He was mistaken there, for she was far happier for having Diamond with her than if she had been wandering about alone. She did not seem so tired as he was.

"Do let us rest a bit " said Diamond.

"Let's see," she answered. "There's something like a railway. Perhaps there's an open arch."

They went toward it and found one, and, better still, there was an empty barrel lying under the arch.

"Hello, here we are!" said the girl. "A barrel's the jolliest bed going—on the tramp, I mean. We'll have forty winks and then go on."

She crept in, and Diamond crept in beside her. They put their arms around each other, and when he began to grow warm Diamond's courage began to come back.

"This *is* jolly!" he said. "I'm *so* glad!"

"I don't think so much of it," said the girl. "I'm used to it, I suppose. But I can't think how a kid like you comes to be out all alone this time o' the night."

She called him a *kid*, but she was not really a month older than he, only she had had to work for her bread and that so soon makes people older.

"But I shouldn't have been out so late if I hadn't got down to help you " said Diamond. "North Wind is gone home long ago."

"You said something about the north wind afore that I couldn't get the rights of." So now, for the sake of his character, Diamond had to tell her the whole story.

She did not believe a word of it. She said she wasn't such a flat as to believe all that bosh. But, as she spoke, there came a great blast of wind through the arch and set the barrel rolling. So they made haste to get out of it.

"I thought we should have had a sleep," said Diamond, "but I can't say I'm very sleepy after all. Let's go on again." They wandered on and on, sometimes sitting on a doorstep, but always turning into lanes or fields when they had a chance.

They found themselves, at last, on a rising ground that sloped rather steeply on the other side. It was a waste kind of spot below, bounded by an irregular wall, with a few doors in it. Outside lay broken things in general, from garden rollers to flowerpots and wine-bottles. But the moment they reached the brow of the rising ground, a gust of wind seized them and blew them down hill as

fast as they could run. Nor could Diamond stop before
he went bang against one of the doors in the wall. To
his dismay it burst open. When they came to themselves
they peeped in. It was the back door of a garden.

"Ah, ah!" cried Diamond, after staring for a few
moments, "I thought so! North Wind takes nobody in!
Here I am in master's garden! I tell you what, little girl,
you just bore a hole in old Sal's wall, put your mouth to

it, and say, 'Please, North Wind, mayn't I go out with you?' Then you'll see what'll come."

"I daresay I shall. But I'm out in the wind too often already to want more of it."

"I said *with* the North Wind, not *in* it."

"It's all one."

"It's *not* all one."

"It *is* all one."

"But I know best."

"And I know better. I'll box your ears " said the girl.

Diamond got very angry. But he remembered that even if she did box his ears, he mustn't box hers again, for she was a girl, and all that boys must do, if girls are rude, is to go away and leave them. So he went in at the door.

"Good-bye, mister," said the girl.

This brought Diamond to his senses. "I'm sorry I was cross," he said. "Come in, and my mother will give you some breakfast."

"No, thank you. I must be off to my crossing. It's morning now."

"I'm very sorry for you " said Diamond.

"Well, it is a life to be tired of—what with old Sal, and so many holes in my shoes," said the girl. "When I think of it, though, I always want to see what's coming next. Good-bye!" She ran up the hill and disappeared behind it. Then Diamond shut the door as he best could, and ran through the kitchen-garden to the stable. And wasn't he glad to get into his own blessed bed again!

Thumbelisa

HANS CHRISTIAN ANDERSEN

THERE was once a woman who had the greatest longing for a tiny little child, but she had no idea where to get one; so she went to an old witch and said to her, "I do so long to have a tiny little child. Will you tell me where I can get one?"

"Oh, we shall be able to manage that," said the witch. "Here is a barley corn for you: it is not at all the same kind as that which grows in the peasant's field, or with which chickens are fed. Plant it in a flowerpot, and you will see what will appear."

"Thank you, oh, thank you!" said the woman, and she gave the witch twelve pennies, then went home and planted the barley corn. A large, handsome flower sprang up at once; it looked exactly like a tulip, but the petals were tightly shut up, just as if they were still in bud. "That is a lovely flower," said the woman, and she kissed the pretty red-and-yellow petals. As she kissed it the flower burst open with a loud snap. It was a real tulip, you could see that; but right in the middle of the flower on the green stool sat a little tiny girl, most lovely and delicate. She was not more than an inch in height, so she was called Thumbelisa.

Her cradle was a smartly varnished walnut shell, with the blue petals of violets for a mattress and a rose leaf to cover her. She slept in it at night, but during the day, she played about on the table where the woman had placed a plate of water surrounded by a wreath of flowers. A large tulip floated on the water, and on this little Thumbelisa sat and sailed about from one side of the plate to the other. She had two white horsehairs for oars. It was a pretty sight.

One night as she lay in her pretty bed, a great ugly toad hopped in at the window, for there was a broken pane. Ugh! How hideous that great, wet toad was! It hopped right down onto the table where Thumbelisa lay fast asleep, under the red rose leaf.

"Here is a lovely wife for my son," said the toad and then she took up the walnut shell, where Thumbelisa slept, and hopped away with it through the window down into the garden. A great, broad stream ran through the garden; but, just at the edge, it was swampy and muddy and it was here that the toad lived with her son. Ugh! How ugly and hideous he was, too, exactly like his mother! "Koax, koax, brekke-ke-kex," that was all he had to say when he saw the lovely, little girl in the walnut shell.

"Do not talk so loud or you will wake her," said the old toad. "She might escape us yet, for she is as light as thistledown! We will put her on one of the broad water-lily leaves out in the stream; it will be just like an island to her, she is so small and light. She won't be able to run away from there while we get the stateroom ready down under the mud, where you and she are to live."

A great many water lilies grew in the stream, their broad, green leaves looked as if they were floating on the surface of the water. The leaf which was farthest from the shore was also the biggest, and, to this one, the old toad swam with the walnut shell in which little Thumbelisa lay. The poor, tiny little creature woke up quite early in the morning, and, when she saw where she was, she began to cry most bitterly, for there was water on every side of the big green leaf and she could not reach the land at any point.

The old toad sat in the mud decking out her home with grasses and the buds of the yellow water lilies, so as to have it very nice for the new daughter-in-law. And then she swam out with her ugly son to the leaf where Thumbelisa stood; they wanted to fetch her pretty bed to place it in the chamber before they took her there. The old toad made a deep curtsy in the water before her, and said, "Here is my son, and you are to live most comfortably with us down in the mud."

"Koax, koax, brekke-ke-kex," was all the son could say.

Then they took the pretty, little bed and swan away with it, but Thumbelisa sat quite alone on the green leaf and cried because she did not want to live with the ugly toad. The little fish which swam about in the water had, no doubt, seen the toad and heard what she said, so they stuck their heads up, wishing to see the little girl. As soon as they saw her, they were delighted with her and were quite grieved to think that she was to go down

to live with the ugly toad. No, that should never happen. They flocked together down in the water round about the green stem which held the leaf she stood upon, and gnawed at it with their teeth till it floated away down the stream, carrying Thumbelisa where the toad could not follow her.

Thumbelisa sailed past place after place, and the little birds in the bushes saw her and sang, "What a lovely, little maid!" The leaf with her on it floated further and further away and, in this manner, reached foreign lands.

A pretty, little white butterfly fluttered 'round and 'round her for some time and at last settled on the leaf, for it had taken quite a fancy to Thumbelisa. She was so happy now, because the toad could not reach her and she was sailing through such lovely scenes; the sun shone on the water and it looked like liquid gold. Then she took her sash and tied one end round the butterfly, and the other, she made fast to the leaf which went gliding

To *A Water Lily*, by Edward MacDowell, gives a melodious picture of the water lily, floating calm and serene on the water as when it held Thumbelisa.

on quicker and quicker and she with it, for she was standing on the leaf. At this moment a big May bug came flying along. He caught sight of her and in an instant, fixed his claw round her slender waist and flew off with her, up into a tree. But the green leaf floated down the stream and the butterfly with it, for he was tied to it and could not get loose.

The May bug settled on the largest leaf on the tree, and fed Thumbelisa with honey from the flowers, and he said that she was lovely although she was not a bit like a May bug. Presently all the other May bugs, who lived in the tree, came to visit them.

They looked at Thumbelisa, and the young lady May bugs twitched their feelers and said, "She has only got two legs! What a poor appearance that makes!" "She has no feelers!" said another. "She is so slender in the waist, fie, she looks like a human being." "How ugly she is," said all the mother May bugs, and yet little Thumbelisa was so pretty. That was certainly also the opinion of the May bug who had captured her; but, when all the others said she was ugly, he began to believe it too and would not have anything more to do with her. She might go wherever she liked! They flew down from the tree with her and placed her on a daisy, where she cried because she was so ugly that the May bugs would have nothing to do with her. And after all, she was more beautiful than anything you could imagine, as delicate and transparent as the finest rose leaf.

OVER THE HILLS

Poor little Thumbelisa lived all the summer quite alone in the wood. She plaited a bed of grass for herself and hung it up under a big dock leaf, which sheltered her from the rain. She sucked the honey from the flowers for her food, and her drink was the dew which lay on the leaves in the morning. In this way the summer and autumn passed, but then came the winter. All the birds, which used to sing so sweetly to her, flew away. The great dock leaf, under which she had lived, shriveled up; and she shivered with the cold, for her clothes were worn out. It began to snow and every snowflake which fell upon her was like a whole shovelful upon one of us, for we are big and she was only one inch in height. Then she wrapped herself up in a withered leaf, but that did not warm her much; she trembled with the cold.

Close to the wood in which she had been living lay a large cornfield, but the corn had long ago been carried away and nothing remained but the bare, dry stubble which stood up out of the frozen ground. The stubble was quite a forest for her to walk about in; oh, how she shook with the cold! Then she came to the door of a Field Mouse's home. It was a little hole down under the stubble. The Field Mouse lived so cosily and warm there, her whole room was full of corn and she had a beautiful kitchen and larder, besides. Poor Thumbelisa stood just inside the door like any other beggar child and begged for a little piece of barley corn, for she had had nothing to eat for two whole days.

"You poor little thing," said the Field Mouse, for she was at bottom a good old Field Mouse. "Come into my warm room and dine with me."

Then, as she took a fancy to Thumbelisa, she said, "You may stay with me for the winter, but you must keep my room clean and tidy and tell me stories, for I am very fond of them," and Thumbelisa did what the good old Field Mouse desired and was, on the whole, very comfortable.

"We shall soon have a visitor " said the Field Mouse. "My neighbour generally comes to see me every weekday. He is even better housed than I am. His rooms are very large and he wears a most beautiful black-velvet coat. If only you could get him for a husband, you would be well settled, but he can't see. You must tell him all the most beautiful stories you know."

But Thumbelisa did not like this, and she would have nothing to say to the neighbour for he was a Mole. He came and paid a visit in his black-velvet coat. He was very rich and wise, said the Field Mouse, and his home was twenty times as large as hers; and he had much learning but he did not like the sun or the beautiful flowers. In fact he spoke slightingly of them, for he had never seen them. Thumbelisa had to sing to the Mole and she sang both "Lady-bug, Lady-bug, fly away home," and "A monk, he wandered through the meadow.'

The Mole had just made a long tunnel through the ground from his house to theirs, and he gave the Field Mouse and Thumbelisa leave to walk in it whenever they liked. He told them not to be afraid of the dead bird which was lying in the passage.

The Mole took a piece of tinderwood in his mouth, for that shines like fire in the dark, and walked in front of them to light them in the long, dark passage. When they came to the place where the bird lay, the Mole thrust his broad nose up to the roof and pushed the earth up so as to make a big hole through which the daylight shone. In the middle of the floor, lay a swallow with its pretty wings closely pressed to its sides and the legs and head drawn in under the feathers. Thumbelisa was so sorry

for it; she loved all the little birds, for they had twittered and sung so sweetly to her during the whole summer. But the Mole kicked it with his short legs and said, "Now it will pipe no more; it must be a miserable fate to be born a little bird! Thank heaven! no child of mine can be a bird!"

Thumbelisa did not say anything; but, when the others turned their backs to the bird, she stooped down and stroked aside the feathers which lay over its head and kissed its closed eyes. "Perhaps it was this very bird which sang so sweetly to me in the summer," she thought. "What pleasure it gave me, the dear, pretty bird."

The Mole now closed up the hole which let in the daylight and conducted the ladies to their home. Thumbelisa could not sleep at all in the night, so she got up out of her bed and plaited a large, handsome mat of hay and then carried it down and spread it all over the bird and laid some soft cotton wool, which she had found in the Field Mouse's room, close 'round its sides, so that it might have a warm bed on the cold ground.

"Good-bye, you sweet little bird," said she, "good-bye, and thank you for your sweet song through the summer when all the trees were green and the sun shone warmly upon us." Then she laid her head close up to the bird's breast, but was quite startled at a sound as if something was thumping inside it. It was the bird's heart. The swallow was not dead but lay there stiff with cold; and, now, that it had been warmed, it began to come to life again.

OVER THE HILLS

In the autumn, all the swallows fly away to warm countries; but, if one happens to be belated, it feels the cold so much that it falls down to the ground and remains lying where it falls till the snow covers it up. The bird was very, very big beside her—Thumbelisa was only one-inch high—but she gathered up her courage, packed the wool closer round it, fetched a leaf which she had used for her own coverlet and laid it over the bird's head. The next night she crept down again to it and found it alive but it could only just open its eyes for a moment to look at Thumbelisa who stood with a bit of tinderwood in her hand, for she had no other lantern.

"Many, many thanks, you sweet child," said the Swallow to her, "you have warmed me beautifully. I shall soon have strength to fly out into the warm sun again."

"Oh!" said she, "it is so cold outside; it snows and freezes; stay in your warm bed and I will tend you." Then she brought water to the Swallow in a leaf, and, when it had drunk some, it told her how it had torn its wing on a blackthorn bush and, therefore, could not fly as fast as the other swallows which were taking flight then for the distant warm lands. At last it fell down on the ground, but after that it remembered nothing and did not in the least know how it had got into the tunnel. It stayed there all the winter, and Thumbelisa grew very fond of it. She did not tell either the Mole or the Field Mouse anything about it, for they did not like the Swallow.

As soon as the spring came and the warmth of the

Sun penetrated the ground, the Swallow said good-bye to Thumbelisa, who opened the hole which the Mole had made above. The sun streamed in deliciously upon them, and the Swallow asked if she would not go with him. She could sit upon his back and they would fly far away into the greenwood. But Thumbelisa knew that it would grieve the old Field Mouse if she left her like that.

"No, I can't," said Thumbelisa.

"Good-bye, good-bye then, you kind, pretty girl," said the Swallow, and flew out into the sunshine. Thumbelisa looked after him and her eyes filled with tears, for she was very fond of the Swallow.

"Tweet, tweet," sang the bird and flew into the greenwood. Thumbelisa was very sad. She was not allowed to go out into the warm sunshine at all. The corn, which was sown in the field near the Field Mouse's house, grew quite long; it was a thick forest for the poor little girl who was only an inch high.

"You must work at your outfit this summer," said the mouse to her, for their neighbour, the tiresome Mole in his black-velvet coat, had asked her to marry him.

"You shall have both woolen and linen, you shall have wherewith to clothe and cover yourself when you go to live with the Mole." Thumbelisa had to turn the distaff and the Field Mouse hired four Spiders to spin and weave day and night. The Mole paid a visit every evening and he was always saying that, when the summer came to an end, the sun would not shine nearly so warmly (now it burnt the ground as hard as a stone). Yes, when the summer was over, he would take her to his home. But Thumbelisa was not at all pleased, for she did not care a bit for the tiresome Mole. Every morning at sunrise and every evening at sunset, she used to creep out to the door, and, when the wind blew aside the tops of the cornstalks so that she could see the blue sky, she thought how bright and lovely it was out there and wished so much to see the dear Swallow again. But, it never came back. No doubt it was a long way off, flying about in the beautiful greenwood.

When the autumn came all Thumbelisa's outfit was ready.

"In four weeks you must be married," said the Field

Mouse to her. But Thumbelisa cried and said that she did not want to go and live with the tiresome Mole.

"Fiddle-dee-dee," said the Field Mouse; "don't be obstinate. You are going to have a splendid husband. The queen, herself, hasn't the equal of his black-velvet coat: both his kitchen and his cellar are full.'

So the Mole had come to fetch Thumbelisa. She was to live deep down under the ground with him and never to go out into the warm sunshine, for he could not bear it. The poor child was very sad at the thought of bidding good-bye to the beautiful sun. While she had been with the Field Mouse, she had at least been allowed to look at it from the door.

"Good-bye, you bright sun," she said as she stretched out her arms toward it and went a little way outside the Field Mouse's house, for now the harvest was over and only the stubble remained. "Good-bye, good-bye!" she said, and threw her tiny arms round a little red flower growing there. "Give my love to the dear Swallow if you happen to see him."

"Tweet, tweet," she heard at this moment above her head. She looked up; it was the Swallow just passing. As soon as it saw Thumbelisa it was delighted; she told it how unwilling she was to live with the ugly Mole deep down underground where the sun never shone. She could not help crying about it.

"The cold winter is coming," said the Swallow, "and I am going to fly away to warm countries. Will you go with me? You can sit upon my back! Tie yourself on with your sash, then we will fly away from the ugly Mole and his dark cavern, far away over the mountains to those warm countries where the sun shines with greater splendor than here, and where it is always summer and there are heaps of flowers. Do fly with me, you sweet little Thumbelisa, who saved my life when I lay frozen in the dark, earthy passage."

"Yes, I will go with you," said Thumbelisa, seating herself on the bird's back with her feet on its outspread wing. She tied her band tightly to one of the strongest feathers, and then the Swallow flew away, high up in the air above forests and lakes, high up above the biggest mountains where the snow never melts; and Thumbelisa crept under the bird's warm feathers and only stuck out her little head to look at the beautiful sights below.

At last they reached the warm countries. The sun shone with a warmer glow; the sky was twice as high; and the most beautiful green and blue grapes grew in clusters on the banks and hedgerows. Oranges and lemons hung in the woods which were fragrant with myrtles and sweet herbs, while beautiful children ran about the roads playing with the large gorgeously-colored butter-flies. But the Swallow flew on and on, and the country grew more and more beautiful. Under magnificent green trees on the shores of the blue sea, stood a dazzling white marble palace of ancient date; vines wreathed them-selves 'round the stately pillars. At the head of these,

there were countless
nests, and the Swallow,
who carried Thumbeli-
sa, lived in one of them.
"Here is my house," said
the Swallow, "but, if you
will choose one of the gor-
geous flowers growing down
there, I will place you in
it, and you will live as
happily as you can wish."

A great, white marble
column had fallen to the
ground and lay there broken in three pieces,
but between these the most lovely, white flowers grew.
The Swallow flew down with Thumbelisa and put her
upon one of the broad leaves. What was her astonishment to find a little man in the middle of the flower.
He had a lovely, golden crown upon his head and the most
beautiful bright wings upon his shoulders. He was no
bigger than Thumbelisa. He was the angel of the flowers.

When the little Prince saw Thumbelisa, he was delighted;
she was the very prettiest maiden he had ever seen. He
therefore took the golden crown off his own head and
placed it on hers. He asked her if she would be his queen
of the flowers! So she said yes to the beautiful Prince;
and, out of every flower, stepped a little lady or a gentleman so lovely that it was a pleasure to look at them. Each

one brought a gift to Thumbelisa, but the best of all was a pair of pretty wings from a large, white fly. They were fastened on her back, and then she, too, could fly from flower to flower. All was then delight and happiness, but the Swallow sat alone in his nest and sang to them as well as he could, for his heart was heavy; he was so fond of Thumbelisa himself, and would have wished never to part from her.

"You shall not be called Thumbelisa," said the angel of the flowers to her; "that is such an ugly name, and you are so pretty. We will call you May."

"Good-bye, good-bye," said the Swallow, and he flew away again from the warm countries, far away back to Denmark. There he had a little nest above the window where the man lived who wrote this story and he sang his "tweet, tweet" to the man, and so we have the whole story.

The Babe of Bethlehem

FROM THE BIBLE

AND it came to pass in those days, that there went out a decree from Caesar Augustus, that all the world should be taxed. And all went to be taxed, every one unto his own city. And Joseph also went up from Galilee, out of the city of Nazareth, into Judæa, unto the city of David, which is called Bethlehem, to be taxed with Mary, his wife, being great with child.

And so it was that, while they were there, the days were accomplished that she should be delivered. And she brought forth her first-born son, and wrapped him in swaddling clothes, and laid him in a manger because there was no room for them in the inn.

And there were in the same country shepherds abiding in the field, keeping watch over their flock by night. And, lo, the Angel of the Lord came upon them, and the glory of the Lord shone round about them, and they were sore afraid. And the Angel said unto them, "Fear not: for, behold, I bring you good tidings of great joy, which shall be to all people. For unto you is born this day, in the city of David, a Saviour, which is Christ the Lord. And this shall be a sign unto you, ye shall find the babe wrapped in swaddling clothes, lying in a manger." And suddenly there was with the Angel a multitude of the Heavenly Host praising God, and saying, "Glory to God in the highest, and on earth peace, good will toward men."

Christmas has always inspired much beautiful music. Favorite Christmas hymns are *Silent Night*, *It Came Upon the Midnight Clear*, *Hark the Herald Angels Sing*, and *While Shepherds Watched*.

And it came to pass, as the angels were gone away from them into Heaven, the shepherds said one to another, "Let us now go even unto Bethlehem, and see this thing which is come to pass."

And they came with haste, and found Mary and Joseph, and the babe lying in a manger. And, when they had seen it, they made known abroad the saying which was told them concerning this child. And all they that heard it wondered at those things which were told them by the shepherds. But Mary kept all these things and pondered them in her heart. And the shepherds returned, glorifying and praising God for all the things that they had heard and seen, as it was told unto them.

Now when Jesus was born in Bethlehem of Judæa, in the days of Herold, the king, behold, there came wise men from the East to Jerusalem, saying, "Where is he that is born King of the Jews? For we have seen his star in the East, and are come to worship him."

When Herod, the king, had heard these things, he was troubled, and all Jerusalem with him.

And, when he had gathered all the chief priests and scribes of the people together, he demanded of them where Christ should be born. And they said unto him, "In Bethlehem of Judæa: for thus it is written by the prophet."

Then Herod, when he had privily called the wise men, enquired of them diligently what time the star appeared.

And he sent them to Bethlehem, and said, "Go and search diligently for the young child; and, when ye have found him, bring me word again that I may come and worship him also." When they had heard the king, they departed; and, lo, the star, which they saw in the East, went before them, till it came and stood over where the young child was. And, when they were come into the house, they saw the young child with Mary, his mother, and fell down and worshiped him; and when they had opened their treasures, they presented unto him gifts—gold and frankincense and myrrh.